SOUTH EAST INSTITUTE OF PUBLIC HEALTH

5 YEARS AT THE
CROSSROADS

Working together in Primary Health and Social Care

PATRICK S DONLAN
DR CHRIS RUSSELL

Foreword by
Don Brand
National Institute for Social Work

British Library Cataloguing in Publication Data
A catalogue record for this book is available from the British Library

ISBN 1 874257620

South East Institute of Public Health
Broomhill House
David Salomons Estate
Broomhill Road
Tunbridge Wells
Kent TN3 0XT

Tel: (01892) 515153
Fax: (01892) 516344

Supported by The NHS Executive, South Thames.

Printed by Optigraph (01892) 668888

CONTENTS

ACKNOWLEDGEMENTS

We would like to thank everyone who took part in the projects from Greenwich, Kent and Bromley, their involvement and assistance with the projects on which these chapters are based was invaluable, without them this book would not have come to fruition. To Brian Morrison, for his attention to detail and for indexing this book. To Lesley Hicken for preparing the manuscript for printing.

FOREWORD

With partnership high on the Government's agenda of priorities, particularly for health and social care, this book is a valuable and timely guide to achieving joint working in practice.

In half a dozen clear and succinct reports, Pat Donlan and Dr Chris Russell distil five years of the South East Institute's practical experience in helping health and social care agencies, and their staff, work together more effectively for the benefit of service users.

The focus is on what works, and on systematic approaches designed to achieve successful outcomes. The reader is able to learn the lessons of other people's experience, to work through the stages of a project from start to finish and understand what needs to be done at each stage to deliver the desired results.

The reports focus on the bread-and-butter activities of organizing health and social care - assessment, commissioning, project management, staff training, building information systems, evaluating results. These are not glamorous topics, but they are some of the basic components of good quality service provision, and they are worth doing properly. They are also the means by which core values and principles can shape and inform service delivery.

"Joined-up thinking" is the current catch-phrase. In these reports, Pat Donlan and Dr Chris Russell draw on the Institute's experience to show how health and social care agencies can become more proficient at joined-up planning, development, training and evaluation. By providing them with the practical tools to improve joint working, the book is also helping to promote the kind of learning culture which supports quality improvements and better outcomes for service users.

Don Brand
National Institute for Social Work

INTRODUCTION

People working together is different from people working singly. It is likely to be more demanding but often enjoys the rewards of being less isolating and more relevant and powerful in its effect.

Working together in health and social care is not difficult, but neither is it easy. The techniques of bringing together the range of professional and voluntary care providers are not immediately transparent to those responsible for planning and implementing new joint services.

This book is designed to help those responsible for or involved in the development of joint health and social care initiatives to benefit from SEIPH's five years experience with these types of community initiatives. Every region, district and locality will have its own advantages as well as difficulties, and the people involved are very likely to represent a range of agencies and organisations with differing agendas. But that is the territory of all health and social care change, where frontiers are being explored, tested and then forced onwards as people experiment with more effective and efficient ways of providing care.

These six papers deal with topics that initiatives such as these must address at some time during the development stages. They are meant to help identify issues which require thought and planning rather than provide specific solutions to operational problems. They may do that, but only where the conditions of new initiatives mirror those experienced by SEIPH in our first 5 years at the crossroads.

THE ROLE OF THE MULTI-AGENCY STEERING GROUP

INTRODUCTION

A steering group has a central role at every stage in any research and development project. In a multi-agency project, the role of the steering group is more complex but does not have to pose special difficulties. This chapter begins by identifying three themes, which appear to be basic to the success of community care projects, and which are therefore worth keeping permanently on the agenda of steering groups. The second section sets out six key tasks to enable steering group members to think through their role and tackle the complex issues which confront them in as clear a way as possible.

THREE THEMES: EMPOWERMENT, EQUALITY AND QUALITY

These three themes, which are inextricably linked, have been identified as central to the success of joint working in community care by a group of researchers who examined six pilot projects in different parts of the UK. The following paragraphs draw on their conclusions. (Smith, R et al (1993) *Working together for better Community Care*, Bristol: SAUS Publications).

Keeping empowerment on the agenda

'Empowerment' is a term which is now fairly widespread in social services but perhaps less frequently referred to in the NHS. Yet the success of joint working in primary health and community care depends on bringing empowerment onto the agenda of everyone involved. Service users and carers will always be disempowered by the failure of agencies and professionals to work together. Whilst the ultimate goal of a truly seamless service may remain elusive, agencies have the task of managing the seams, rather than passing the buck. So the first empowering thing for agencies to do is to tackle the business of working together.

User empowerment is a slow process. It depends on people in the community taking their power and using it, and upon professionals actively supporting this rather than fearing and sabotaging it. The role of the steering group is to ensure that multi-agency projects are moving in the right direction, without being over-optimistic about how long the process might take: if each project is closer to an empowerment model than the last, this is an achievement to be proud of. Keeping empowerment on the agenda both literally and metaphorically is the main thing.

To keep empowerment on the agenda:

- **Be aware of the national policy agenda and its implications for local implementation, in particular:**

  1. a preference for joint community care plans by health and social services;

  2. formal requirements for public consultation;

  3. the obligation on health professionals to participate in the care management process;

  4. active participation of users and carers in the assessment of their needs;

  5. the provision of information about services in order to extend choice [to consumers].

- **Check links with NHS initiatives such as Patients' Charter**

- **Ask how the project will enhance users' choice**

- **Talk through how users will be involved in the project:**

  1. in the design (setting objectives; choosing location etc.);

  2. in the evaluation

  3. in decisions about further development

- **Reflect periodically on how the steering group's understanding of empowerment is changing as the project unfolds**

- **Include empowerment as one of the key criteria against which to evaluate the success of the project:**

  1. How well has the project worked in supporting empowerment?

  2. How has user and carer involvement affected the project's development?

  3. What lessons have been learnt (How will you do things next time?)

Keeping equality on the agenda

Equality of opportunity and access is a second vital ingredient. This includes ensuring that joint working arrangements introduced by multi-agency projects explicitly tackle the levels of exclusion, inequality and prejudice which are all too easily institutionalised in working practices. Certain groups of people who are likely to be excluded from primary care, such as homeless people and refugees, are those who are likely to be in most need, including need for community care. Similarly, people whose access to primary care services may be restricted because of their physical, intellectual, language or communication needs will require community care services just as they need primary health care services. Finally, many people from black and other minority ethnic groups experience prejudice and misunderstanding when they use primary care services, and this experience is compounded if they are also elderly, young, or poor: once again, they are likely to have community care needs as well as primary health care needs, and experiences of prejudice in one will affect their uptake of the other.

Equal opportunities are central to working together for community care because of the implications for:

- who is involved
- how needs are identified
- how resources are allocated
- how decisions can be made about priorities
- how innovative practices can be established
- how good quality of service can be delivered

If they do not address the issue of equality from the outset, projects miss out on the benefit of input at the earliest possible stage from groups who are otherwise likely to be marginalised. This has the result that those groups will be expected to make do with styles and forms of service provision that appear to be acceptable to the majority population. Good practice is likely to be promoted when managers and professionals identify with service users from minority groups. This does not, it is worth noting, work for all age groups, as elderly people, children and young people are not represented among groups of managers and professionals. This makes the inclusion of, for example, elderly service users, even more important. Disabled people, and many minority ethnic groups, are also very under-represented in management and professional teams.

The likely barriers to equality are:

1. failure to take this aspect of service commissioning and provision into account at all;

2. unclear policy, strategy and practice procedures within agencies, making it difficult or impossible to identify a shared policy agenda for equal opportunities for the project;

3. embarrassment or uncertainty about equal opportunities, leading to a resistance to address the issues raised; this had the effect of further marginalising equality issues.

These barriers to equality can be overcome by positive action; ensuring accountability; developing training strategies; working together at every stage to share power and responsibility; mutual respect and sustained commitment.

In practice, all this requires clear policies and practices: acceptance of the principle of self-determination; developing shared meanings about equal rights, and carers; resourcing empowerment strategies; creating monitoring and evaluation systems on equality; a capacity for organisations to learn, including from mistakes; a commitment to building mutual respect and trust through the development of networks and alliances.

Keeping quality on the agenda

Quality is a term used so frequently that its meaning has been devalued, yet for people who need services, quality is of paramount importance: quality of information, quality of assessment of their needs, quality of care planning and quality of relationships with the professional people whose role is to enable them to access services. Putting users and carers at the centre of the community care equation includes recognising that, for them, quality means being listened to, having a greater sense of control, and having more knowledge of the options available and of what is happening.

Power-sharing and mutual trust are central to quality care which is recognised as such by users and carers. In their analysis of six community care projects, Smith *et al* (1993) identified two main causes of difficulty in providing quality care.

1   The commonly held belief that only professional staff were in a position to define what was needed and what type of service was required;

2   Resources continued to be viewed as a central factor, even though the way in which people treat each other is not in itself dependent on resources.

Examples of quality services identified in the projects included:

- a right to be heard on the part of users and carers;

- the creation of a warm, welcoming, non-stigmatising environment so that individuals were less likely to be wary of approaching a particular service;

- clear, practical foundations for introducing quality into everyday activities, whether at the level of planning, managing, delivering or evaluating services.

Three practical lessons emerged:

1. Definitions of quality need to be based on clear values and objectives, which put the rights of   users and carers first, and are not determined solely by professionals.

2. Pilot projects can be useful for improving the quality of care, but adopting short, fixed timescales is likely to lead to failure, and if the projects are resource intensive, the resource implications for mainstream developments need to be overtly recognised.

3. User-led service quality can develop only with a reframing of the professional role, to emphasise giving information and explaining the options available; coordinating and negotiating rather than assessing; and recognising that control of decisions lies with the user or carer.

SIX TASKS

Creating a group of people from different backgrounds and perspectives and expecting that group to begin immediately to steer the strategic direction of a multi-agency project and pay constant heed to the themes of empowerment, equality and quality is a tall order. Being a fully active member of a steering group is both demanding and time consuming. Yet members of such groups are usually expected to accomplish great things without any previous experience of working together or even of working with other agencies and often without having the time or space to form themselves into a task-focused team. In this respect, they may well be going through a similar experience to that of the multi-disciplinary teams within the projects they are steering.

They also probably share the experience of some, if not all, project team members in that their involvement in the group is not a central role for which adequate time has been set aside, but rather just one more part of a busy schedule which has to somehow be fitted in "because joint working is a good idea". However, steering group members have a specific disadvantage in that they meet relatively rarely (usually monthly at most, if not bi-monthly or quarterly) and most of their activity happens within their respective organisations between meetings crammed, once again, amidst a host of other equally demanding tasks.

The ideal model of a steering group, having time and space to progressively build up knowledge, trust and confidence before embarking on a bound-to-be-successful project is rarely possible in practice, it seems. So while the six tasks set out here are presented as successive stages, it is fully understood that they are much more likely to be performed in a less systematic way, sometimes simultaneously, sometimes consecutively, and sometimes in a different order. What is important is that members of multi-agency groups appreciate that they must pay attention to all of these tasks, and failure to do so will to some extent compromise the success of the group, and therefore of the project.

Multi-agency Project Steering Groups: Key Tasks

1.   Decide who is going to be involved and how

2.   Identify a shared agenda

3.   Decide on the overall purpose of the project and stick to it

4.   Set clear, achievable and measurable or observable objectives and be prepared to review them

5.   Design an evaluation that includes everyone

6.   Listen to the findings and act on them: promote the learning organisation

Task 1.   Decide who is going to be involved and how

There is a tendency in setting up project steering groups to focus on the statutory agencies, and to emphasise commissioning over service provision. At the same time, steering group members are often at pains to emphasise the importance of identifying and achieving outcomes for service users (not so often for carers). What about the other stakeholders being directly involved on the steering group? Often the justification for limiting membership, particularly in the early days of new joint working arrangements, is that the principal agencies need to get their act together first. They may feel that in this way they will be able to present a coherent project to other parties who might be involved later. The down side of this is that other important stakeholders may not be directly involved at the crucial stages of agreeing the overall purpose, setting objectives and designing the action research. By the time they are invited in, they may feel even more disempowered and marginalised.

If it is decided to restrict membership in a way which excludes any potential stakeholders, then it will be especially important to decide how their views will be sought, recorded and acted upon. This may include for example having standard items on the agenda, or holding regular or occasional "whole project" meetings where wider participation is sought and opportunities for catching up and joining in are created. Without some mechanism in place to ensure that equal weight is given to different perspectives whatever the composition of the steering group, the group is likely to get so bogged down with issues of inter-agency organisational incompatibility and intra-agency professional tribalism (eg between different client group interests or different disciplines) that there is no time or space to consider how to ensure that what matters to the services users and carers is really being addressed. What matters to them is empowerment, equality and quality.

Box 1:1 lists the most likely stakeholders. You will need to modify the list, taking into account all organisations and groups who might be affected by the project in some way. Then the full list can be used to decide how they will all be involved, for example; by being permanent members of the Steering Group; occasional or regular guests; or by being kept informed and invited to participate in the evaluation. How else might they be involved? Make sure to talk this through.

Statutory Organisations

Local authorities

These are vast organisations with an over-arching corporate structure sometimes employing thousands of people across several departments. London Borough Councils, Metropolitan Councils and the new Unitary Authorities provide the full range of services, while in other areas some services (such as social services and education) are provided by County Councils while others (including housing) are provided by smaller District Councils. Social Services Departments are large organisations in themselves, and are often divided into sections that cover very different aspects of work. Communication and working arrangements can vary widely within and between sections - make no assumptions! Major divisions exist in most departments, for example, between services for children and those for adults, the former focusing on child protection and the latter on community care. Most Social Services Departments are still important providers of services as well as being responsible for assessment of individuals' needs and commissioning to meeting the needs of the population they serve (which may vary from about 200,000 to over one million). In addition to Social Services, there are other local authority departments to be considered in relation to primary and community care, most notably Housing.

Box : 1.1   **Identifying the stakeholders**

statutory organisations

Local authorities
Health authorities
NHS trusts
Primary care practices
Community Health Councils (CHCs)

voluntary organisations

Formally constituted non-profit making organisations, usually with charitable status; may be national or local, large or small, with broad or narrow focus; include campaigning/lobbying organisations and those providing services (or both).

community groups

Usually informal, self determining groups, representing interests of local community or particular minorities; may be action groups or lobbying groups.

Health authorities

These are usually smaller organisations in terms of personnel, and are responsible solely for commissioning services. Their core task is to ensure that the optimum quantity and quality of health services and health improvement activities is being purchased through their contracts with NHS Trusts and other external organisations; through non-contractual relationships with primary care personnel including GPs; and through partnerships with health-related bodies such as local authorities and voluntary organisations. Like Social Services, they have a geographically defined population base, and they can cover large populations and geographical areas; they may operate a commissioning process, based on smaller localities.

NHS trusts

These are large provider organisations for health care services and other related activities such as health promotion. Two main categories are *acute trusts* (usually centred on a former district general hospital) and *community trusts* (providing services outside hospital, such as community nursing, learning disability services, and so on). The populations they serve are not restricted by geographical borders, but are determined by the contracts placed with them by health authorities and fundholding GPs.

Primary care practices

GPs and the staff employed directly by them practice nurses, practice managers and receptionists, as well as sessional staff such as complementary therapists and counsellors provide primary health care services to all patients registered with the practice. GPs may operate single handed or in groups, with each partner providing care for a discrete group of patients, with arrangements for covering each others' patients list as necessary. GP practices fall into two types fundholding and non-fundholding depending upon whether they have a direct role in commissioning some secondary care services for their patients. Fundholding practices may be linked with others through consortium or multi-fund arrangements. In addition to providing services, and in the case of fundholding practices commissioning some services through NHS trusts, all primary care practices should have a role in planning services for their locality, in conjunction with health authorities, local authorities and other organisations. Dentistry, pharmacy and optometry are also important parts of primary care provision. Largely operating through private outlets (including pharmaceutical departments in supermarkets, high street opticians and so on), their role in community care and their perspective on how different working arrangements affect patient access to services is often overlooked.

Community health councils (CHCS)

Community Health Councils are statutory bodies set up to represent the interests of patients in the NHS. They are autonomous organisations and comprise a group of around twenty voluntary members (appointed by local authorities, voluntary organisations and the NHS Executive) and a small staff group of perhaps three or four paid officers. A typical CHC might cover the patient population of one health authority, or of a part of a health authority area. The workload is carried by the paid officers and by the body of members, some of whom represent other organisations. Although their statutory rules of engagement do not extend beyond the NHS, in practice they are increasingly and inevitably becoming involved with local authority activity through the joint working around community care, for example.

Voluntary Organisations

These are non-statutory, not-for-profit organisations, formally bound by a constitution which sets out their aims and the scope of their activity. They may be campaigning or lobbying bodies, or they may be service providers, or a combination of the two. Increasingly, over the past decade or so, the relationship between statutory and non-statutory bodies has moved from one of patronage and grants to one of partnership and direct contracts. The term "voluntary organisation", which implies independence and charitable status, covers an enormous range in terms of size, scope and complexity. This includes well-known large organisations such as Age Concern, Save the Children, MIND, and SCOPE, with a large national (or international) component and local counterparts, as well as small national or local organisations with specific focus on, for example, head injury services or coeliac disease. In being invited to form partnerships to plan services or steer projects, voluntary organisations - particularly the smaller ones face the challenge of limited staffing to attend and carry out follow up action meetings. Sometimes umbrella organisations such as Councils for Voluntary Service (CVS) or specific local forums can provide the right level of input.

Community Groups

Community groups are not necessarily formally constituted, and are likely to be locally self determining. The extent of special interest groups and action groups within a local area varies. There are likely to be many more in inner city areas, for example, than in suburban or rural locations. Simply identifying the groups in your area may be a major exercise, although arguably a very worthwhile one. One London borough coordinator of joint projects, for example, reported that there were literally hundreds of community groups, representing some highly specialised interests, many of these being extremely relevant to local joint agency developments. Involving community groups is probably best seen as an evolutionary process: being alert to their existence and their potential role, and informing them of your activities, is the first step.

General considerations

Having decided which organisations and groups are to be included in the steering group, it is important, firstly, that their representatives are able to make decisions on behalf of the organisation or group they are representing. This will mean having sufficient seniority or having good enough access to the decision-making process in their organisation. Secondly, it is important that steering group members attend meetings and other project events regularly, and that permanent deputies are appointed to stand in if absolutely necessary. In this way continuity is secured. Thirdly, it is important that members are supported for example through facilitated training sessions so that they know enough about each others' organisations, roles and responsibilities, about the background to the project, and about the way in which action research works.

Finally, it is worth bearing in mind that membership of the steering group <u>will</u> change during the course of the project, either by design, as new organisations are invited to join, or by default, as members leave their posts, for example. Whenever a member leaves the group, some experience is lost. Whenever a new member joins, he or she will need to be brought up to date and properly introduced to the project. Explaining the project (its aims and objectives, how it works, and the operational obstacles which have been tackled) is often a good opportunity for the steering group to review the project and reflect on progress.

Task 2   Identify a shared agenda

Being aware of your own agency's agenda and working together to develop a shared agenda are important tasks in their own right, but they are usually tackled together. The wider the representation on the steering group, the more likely it is that everyone's agenda will be taken into account, and the longer it will probably take to work through this process. Given the usual need to press on with the operational development of the project, this process may well have to continue along the way, which may feel uncomfortable from time to time. Having users and carers involved at an early stage will help to ensure that the agenda is set from their perspective, bearing in mind the points made above about empowerment, equality and quality, rather than professionally driven.

Converting a set of partially overlapping, partially diverging (or even conflicting) professionally and managerially driven agendas from different statutory agencies into a shared agenda which puts users and carers at the centre is an extremely demanding task. Be very suspicious if this appears to have been accomplished after just two or three meetings. The chances are the resulting shared agenda will be merely a starting point probably taking the form of a "lowest-common-denominator" approach with a nod towards the importance of users and carers. This is a good enough starting point, but a lot more is needed. All too often, the push to get the project up and running becomes an excuse to avoid the more in-depth work required. Yet from experience it is clear that getting projects off the ground takes at least several months if not a full year: this time could be used well to develop a shared sense of purpose.

Task 3.   Decide on the overall aim of the project and stick to it

If the operational demands of getting the project up and running can be held back to allow time to develop a shared agenda that truly puts users and carers at the centre of the project, this third task is likely to be achieved much more successfully. This represents a crucial stage, because the timing is critical: the central aim of the project needs to be decided and then kept central throughout the duration of the project. The central aim is essentially a one sentence answer to the question "What do we want the project to achieve?". However, it is important to remember that if this is couched in professional or managerial terms, then even if the inter-agency differences have been ironed out, it will be impossible to place users and carers at the centre of the project, and ultimately the outcomes will be managerial, and professionally meaningful rather than genuinely geared to people's needs. Once again, involving users and carers from the beginning and listening to their views is the easiest way to guarantee success.

Task 4   Set clear, achievable, and measurable or observable objectives and be prepared to review them

It is the overall aim of the project that is sacred, not the objectives. The essence of a developmental project is just that: it is developmental. Sometimes people are so concerned about retaining the original objectives that they choose to keep them even when they seem to be becoming irrelevant to what is actually going on in the project. In fact, it is better to explicitly review and modify objectives where necessary in the light of lessons learnt so far in the project.

Task 5.   Design an evaluation that works for everyone

The steering group has a vital role in all stages of the evaluation. Here the focus is on the design stage. Above all, the group has to ensure that all perspectives are taken into account. This means looking carefully at the list of stakeholders and deciding how each of their perspectives might be included, and how to ensure that the evaluation encompasses the anticipated benefits and costs for everyone. The ten steps involved in designing an evaluation using an action research approach are set out in the later chapter EVALUATION DESIGN AND ACTION RESEARCH.

Task 6.   Listen to the findings and act on them: promote the learning organisation

The steering group has a role in ensuring that what is learnt from the project is put into practice, thereby promoting the learning organisation. In an action research project, findings are incorporated into the learning process in a gradual, incremental way. This is different from the traditional situation where research findings are "handed over" at the end of the project with a set of recommendations. In a research and development project, then, decisions are being made on the basis of evaluation findings all the way through. However it is also the case that decisions are often also made without any reference at all to the evaluation findings. It is this ongoing and unstoppable process of development that action research attempts to address however imperfectly.

For example, in a multi-agency project that set out to test two different models of joint working, with each taking place on a number of separate pilot sites (primary care practices), the evaluation researcher soon uncovered the fact that working practices were not only varying significantly from one model to another (as had been intended) but also from one pilot site to another within the same model. Subsequently, this complexity became compounded as a result of a decision to ultimately move towards a third "middle path" model of integrating primary health and social care, by aligning small teams of social care managers with clusters of primary care practices: the care managers would maintain a social services office base but would deal directly with referrals relating to the corresponding primary care practices. This decision was made for expedient political and practical reasons, and the evaluation was understandably expected to give some insight into how well this model might work, a task which was not without difficulties! Even the most flexible action research design will be challenged by the inevitable twists and turns of mid-project policy decisions. It is the task of the steering group to make sure that the evaluation is neither hijacked by new demands nor jettisoned too early for worthwhile findings to emerge.

...and finally

Whilst the primary tasks of the steering group relate to the particular project they came together to steer, they have an important function in promoting and supporting a fundamental re-think of agencies' roles in relation to primary and community care. Yet how far can the steering group go in shaping future direction within agencies? Do they have a role in this at all? In practice, it seems that they are more reticent about tackling intra-agency issues than inter-agency ones, and this has the overall effect of slowing down developments in community care.

Multi-agency project steering groups clearly have a potential role in developing new ways of thinking within agencies as well as between them. They have a role in developing new styles of leadership and also in providing opportunities for new types of professionalism to emerge. First and foremost, they have a role in enabling service users and carers from all groups within the community to take their central place in determining the future direction of all of these aspects of care.

PROJECT MANAGEMENT AT THE CROSSROADS OF HEALTH AND SOCIAL CARE

INTRODUCTION

Health and social care services exist in splendid segregation in many cases. Separately funded, with diverse professional traditions and often located at some distance from one another within the same locality, their workings seem more a product of their distinctive organisational structures than their purposes. The reality is, of course, that those most in need of health services often require social care services as well. The frail elderly, people with physical disabilities, and those with mental health problems are likely to require services which are interdependent. In other words, the provision of health services is essential to the success of social care, whilst social care services can ensure the long term effectiveness of health care services. When these services are provided in isolation they are less likely to meet the needs of the patient or service user.

The coming together of health and social care services seems an obvious solution to the problem of providing services to people with complex and special needs. It is none the easier for that, though. Experience has shown that bringing together professionals from different traditions and organisational cultures is a task requiring strong managerial skills. This paper reflects on SEIPH's experience in the project management, training and evaluation of projects establishing:

- linked or attached social care managers for older people within primary health care settings;

- multi-disciplinary community mental health teams;

- attached children and families social workers in primary care settings;

- social outcome monitoring systems within multi-professional teams for people with learning disabilities.

People with complex health and social care needs can be disadvantaged by the very care systems which exist for their benefit. Because care is often provided by different agencies for distinct and often dissimilar purposes, the service user is "seen" differently by each agency or group of professionals.

Health and social care agencies tend to have different objectives, histories and cultures and this leads to diverse understandings of the needs of individual service users. Often there is no understanding of the needs of the "whole person."

Planning services for people whose health and social needs are complex and interwoven is a demanding task. Simplistic, single agency interventions will inevitably fail to address the needs of the whole person. Agencies working together, each providing services which coordinate with other services, create better opportunities for meeting the needs of the individual service user. A policy which unites the intentions and the energies of service providers is likely to be more successful in meeting the needs of the whole person.

Health and social care agencies can only learn to work together by working together. Creation of joint policy documents, and the whole of the community care planning activity, remain sterile and meaningless unless agencies are prepared to welcome each other's point of view and to accept that the needs of the service users are paramount. Learning to acknowledge, respect and trust the skills of other professionals is the task of any initiative bringing together health and social care services. Developing shared services, which service users experience as seamless (even though the professionals involved are busily managing the "seams" in the background) is the training ground and the proving ground of successful joint working.

Joint working in this way is not difficult but it is different! All those involved are to some degree leaving behind the familiar and the comfortable. Because every professional agency will be experiencing the need for change, it is commonly accepted that a project manager be appointed to ensure that the processes of change are coherent, integrative and effective.

This paper identifies the importance of project management in the change processes involved in creating effective joint health and social care services.

INDEPENDENT PROJECT MANAGEMENT IN MULTI-DISCIPLINARY SETTINGS

Project management in multi-disciplinary settings is a formally structured process which takes forward organisational change or service development amongst or between organisations. It is a comprehensive enterprise incorporating the planning and management of joint services with the ongoing monitoring and evaluation of progress. Because project management is closely linked with the information collection requirements of evaluation, information about service effectiveness is available throughout the life of the project rather than only toward the closing months. This means that remedial action can be taken when required to keep the project to its objectives and schedule.

Project management differs from other forms of change in as much as it is entirely focussed on effectiveness (outcome). While not excluding the practical considerations which necessarily arise during any process of change, project management is effectively defined by the outcome it seeks to achieve. Although project management addresses the processes of change, such as policy formation, strategic and tactical thinking, implementation, monitoring, review and evaluation, its aim is fundamentally to bring about benefits that would not be available to service users if their care agencies went on working independently. So while joint policies are essential to good joint working, and shared procedures are crucial to reducing duplication and increasing effectiveness, the success of project management will be judged by the benefits it generates for the service users as well as the care agencies involved.

Project management becomes a powerful tool when it enjoys independence from the project's participants. Whilst this may not be necessary in every multi-disciplinary project, experience shows that service user outcomes and organisational benefits are highest when agencies form a partnership of equals. Without this degree of independence, one participating agency can feel that it is "working to" the agenda of another. The vital sense of urgency and ownership, so necessary to successful service development, can be lost.

Independent project management, where the project management team is commissioned and/or responsible to a number of participating agencies, provides a practical and functional alternative. The competitive mentality implicit in the "mixed economy" philosophy of the early 1990s is beginning to evolve against the background of pervasive funding limitations and trust mergers. Because independent project management remains outside the line management structure of any single agency, the complementarity of health and social care provision is promoted. This model occupies the middle ground between agencies and ensures that the desired outcome is a product of the efforts of all participating agencies.

In independent project management the emphasis is on action, providing direction rather than solutions. Many health and social care agencies are slow to respond to service user need because of the complexity of their communications, their comprehensive procedures, their size. Major organisational structure changes must take place while agencies continue to provide services to users, fragmenting staff time, energy and focus. This can slow the required responses to change that are imperative to the efficient introduction of new service methods. Little is stable in organisations during periods of great change, so effective project management keeps the action rolling and its relevance apparent to all participants.   Organisational sluggishness is no longer mistaken for organisational stability.

The problems associated with implementing new services, procedures and structures do not exist in a static culture. The boundaries of these problems are likely to change during the problem solving process itself.   The change process itself changes! New ideas, however creative and efficient, require translation into the language currently used by all participating agencies if they are to be fully understood and accepted. Successful project management anticipates these changes and the operational requirements which flow from them.

THE ROLE OF THE STEERING GROUP

There are several reasons why agencies commission project management services for health and social care developments:

*   inexperience in project management;

*   inexperience in joint working;

*   lack of confidence in working in detail;

*   lack of clarity about what is really needed;

*   experience of poor relationships amongst agencies;

*   recognized expertise of project manager.

Multi-disciplinary service development projects are likely to be commissioned by several agencies, with funding from all or only one of the participating agencies. Such a commissioning process carries with it the danger that each agency may only be able or willing to seek project outcomes which support its own organisational needs and objectives. Unless there is a mechanism to recognize the benefits for all the agencies and prioritize those which they all share, project management will be diluted into satisfying only parochial and not collective expectations.

Project steering groups have a significant role to play in building effective joint planning relationships amongst health and social care agencies. The purpose of the steering group is to provide authoritative guidance for the project. Members will represent the agencies involved in the review and be of a sufficiently senior status within their agencies to facilitate timely decision making that may be necessary during the project and access to information as required by the project management team.

The members of the steering group have clear roles which require them to work corporately. As a group, it is their responsibility to:

- commission the work of the project, including the project management;

- provide resources for the work of the project;

- provide guidance and direction during the life of the project;

- receive regular reports from the project management team, which remains responsible for the day-to-day progress of the project.

More specifically, the steering group has a number of functions which include:

- acting as a forum for considering the met and unmet needs of service users;

- receiving reports from the project manager and taking decisions as required relating to the completion of the project;

- providing access to relevant personnel and documentation as required;

- ensuring the continuity and consistency of analysis provided during the project;

- ensuring appropriate integration of relevant epidemiological information into the interim and final reports of the project management team;

- identifying organisational requirements and constraints relating to current or future service provision or commissioning processes;

- identifying potential strategies for new or existing service developments based on the findings of the interim and final reports of the project management team;

- facilitating communication within the representative agencies about the relevance and progress of the project;

- reviewing the project management team's reports and recommendations on behalf of all participating agencies;

- recognising the implications of the recommendations for resources, and probable implementation issues including training requirements and timescales.

An active and committed steering group is essential to the long term success of any multi-disciplinary development project. So that it remains active, steps must be taken to minimize the workload and time commitment demands of membership by:

- clarifying the terms of reference of the group as early as possible;

- providing written agendas to all members at least two weeks before meetings;

- strictly limiting the duration of meetings (maximum 1.5 hours);

- attaching meetings to already existing forums attended by key steering group members (existing joint planing groups, etc);

- provide effective chairing of meetings from within the membership of the steering group.

Another practical measure would be that of the project management team taking responsibility for providing the required administrative support for the steering group.

THE ROLE OF THE PROJECT MANAGER

It is essential that the project manager is <u>not</u> a representative member of the steering group. The project manager has four roles in attending steering group meetings:

- to inform the group about current progress of the project;

- to take instruction about developments and problem solving relating to the project;

- to facilitate negotiation within the steering group about operational or policy issues which arise during the course of the project;

- to identify new opportunities for joint working.

The project manager may lead a small team of workers, depending on the size and complexity of the project. Whatever the working arrangements, the project management task is to work with each agency as they participate in the project(s). Where multi-disciplinary development projects are complex and take on differing operational features reflecting changing local circumstances, the project manager must ensure that all the developments are coordinated.

Project coordination is a major feature of the project manager's work. The main themes of any effective coordination process are **clarity, communication and confirmation.**

Clarity

Clarity is surprisingly uncommon in many projects. Without clarity good ideas and good intentions fall away into chaos and resentfulness, and the need to clarify must be revisited regularly during the life of any multi-disciplinary project. There is a golden rule which, in practice, is not always easy to apply: progress through each stage of a project must only follow a renewed understanding of the purposes of the project. As the project develops, each stage requires the participants (steering group as well as locally based participants) to reaffirm the common purposes and intended benefits of the project.

The search for clarity has many facets:

words and their agreed meanings The word "assessment", for example, can mean an in-depth process to some whilst signifying nothing more than a simple screening to others;

roles and responsibilities Who can and will make decisions, who is best placed to influence others;

the project plan for the overall project and its local initiatives:
aims
objectives
working practices
defined agency relationships
defined communication systems and networks
intended benefits and outcomes
evaluation methods and data sources for measuring success

<u>the implementation strategy</u> - the delivery of the project plan, taking into account local circumstances and timing;

<u>training requirements for personnel involved in the project;</u>

<u>mechanisms for reporting to the steering group during the life of the project.</u>

Communication

Communication is always identified as a prerequisite for successful project management, yet is often assumed that current communication systems in and amongst participating agencies are adequate and appropriate for a multi-disciplinary project. Health and social care agencies function for different though related purposes, so it is unlikely that existing communication customs and forums will provide the effective "read-across" experience required by the project.

The content of inter-agency communication requires nothing more than organisational and presentational skills, provided that the content is relevant. It is important that the content of communication is influenced by the demands of the project evaluation. It is the strategies of communication which require management.

There are three levels of communication which require some strategic thinking: person to person; person to agency; agency to public.

Person to person

Without effective person to person communication, the project easily becomes functionally uneventful. Because of diverse traditions and training histories and professional perspectives, multi-disciplinary projects require both time and the opportunity for participants to learn each other's language, and hopefully realize the importance of other perspectives on services. Professionals are often much more able (and sometimes, willing) to communicate with service users than with each other. Joint information, training and project feedback forums provide useful channels for making communication easier.

Person to agency
Each participant in a multi-disciplinary project has at least one agency to relate to, whether it be their own or others. The same problems apply here as apply to person to person communication. The agency may be speaking a different language because

of its traditional or restricted view of what is pertinent to their role. There are two important considerations here:

> When communicating with another agency, every participant must understand how the people in that agency think, what they feel is important, and how central they see their participation in the project as being. It is useful to think through what ways of communicating with other agencies will be seen by them as helpful;

> When communicating within one's own organisation, it is essential to remember that there are likely to be many people not represented on the steering group or project team, whose work will in some way be affected by the project. It is important to identify those people and develop information or communication strategies that give assurance that their support will be forthcoming.

Agency to public

This is often not addressed, simply because multi-disciplinary project development is seen to be an activity for professionals. By developing habits of communicating with service users and the general public, formally and informally the professional has access to the answers to the ultimate evaluation question: "So what?" If projects are to produce tangible effects as well as more efficient and cost effective processes, the public has to be a major stakeholder. Representation on the steering group is a good start, but not enough in itself. Engaging the public and service users from the outset and throughout the project's progress provides a discipline which is more likely to be successful and relevant.

Confirmation

Confirmation means ensuring that the planned activities and processes are in fact in place. The project manager not only ensures that tasks are assigned, but completed and relates to other important processes of the project. Confirmation primarily relates to verifying that agreed processes are in place, whereas evaluation seeks to identify the effectiveness of those processes.

Agencies accustomed to working with each other often do so on their own terms rather than by shared "rules" of engagement. Joint working can become piecemeal and peripheral to what each agency deems to be its major activities. Through the project manager role the terms of engagement become joint terms, managed by an independent "authority" to effect the jointly beneficial outcomes. The project manager occupies the middle ground amongst agencies, using the position and its authority to effect changes that each agency singly would find difficult to achieve.

UNDERSTANDING CURRENT AND NEW ACTIVITY: FUNCTIONAL ANALYSIS

Understanding how each of the participating organisations works is fundamental to establishing new ways in which they can interrelate. Whilst this is something which "unfolds" during the whole of the project, it is crucial that the project manager apply some consistent methodology for developing greater functional understanding from the earliest stages of the project. Here is a five stage model for activity analysis, with the results of each stage informing the work of the others.

Collecting information about each participating agency or pilot team aims to identify major operational objectives and processes as well as distinctive characteristics associated with already existing service provision. Reviews of current documentation such as community care plans, policy documents and relevant legislation or government guidelines provides the basis for the remaining stages of functional analysis.

Identifying systems or processes, information flows and communication patterns which make up the activity of each of the participating agencies. Systems could best be understood as "threads" of activities that are linked together in a way which is intended to meet determined objectives. It is important to identify how each agency acts within itself and in relation to other agencies and the public. Structured interviews with key agency personnel, or a brainstorming session, can usually help identify and clarify the systems which exist and give some understanding of how those systems interrelate.

Modelling activities involves experimenting with the sequence and logical connections between activities in a system. Here the project manager develops conceptual "models" of what should be happening, not what is actually happening. These models form the basis of discussion with participating agencies as to what future joint activity should look like. Following this discussion and the negotiation which inevitably follows, these models are merged into the overall vision of future service delivery.

Deriving characteristics from the newly merged conceptual models aims to identify the most significant features necessary for interlinking the models. Data collection, information flows and communication processes are usually identified as shared linkages between activity models, but it is important also to recognize specific capabilities that staff should share in the multi-disciplinary initiative. This stage will also identify how the larger issues, such as skill mix and organisational structures, may need to be modified to achieve the best outcomes for the joint initiative.

Comparing models with existing activity will identify the gaps between the vision and reality. This will help prioritise project management activity by identifying:

the systems which do not need to be changed;

the systems which can be changed with little or no difficulty;

changes which are likely to require significant investment of time, energy and money;

changes which are not likely to be possible in the foreseeable future.

Functional analysis examines current activity in light of the demands of a future service delivery pattern. The conceptual models relate possible future activity to existing systems in order to identify the organisational requirements of the future. Future activity is clearly linked to the achievement of future objectives.

PROJECT PLANNING

Planning a project is much like spreading a map across a table. It is essential to agree both the starting points and the intended destination. But it is the steps and stops along the way that must be identified, and even then even the best of scouts will have limited information about what might happen in the future to change the plans. Competing organisational objectives can impede progress. So project planning is more than just establishing and agreeing a strategy, it is also about planning every day to cope with the uncontrollable demands, unrecognized difficulties and unintended consequences of change that arise as the project progresses.

Project management could be described as the application of strategy to practical realities. If strategy is the map, planning is the making of reservations and the packing. Project planning of multi-disciplinary initiatives is likely to focus on service maintenance or service innovation, and it is crucial that all participants are agreed as to which type of planning is being engaged in. Maintenance planning aims to continue current activity with fewer resources, by reducing overheads and duplication and by changing working relationships amongst agencies. Innovative planning, on the other hand, aims to enhance current activity within the same or fewer resources. Innovative projects are likely to experiment with alternative service provision models, and this requires acceptance that higher levels of risk will require monitoring and management.

Multi-disciplinary initiatives exist within a political context, so planning will have a political perspective. Though much of the political animosity is likely to remain within the steering group, the project planning process must remain rigorous about these four political considerations:

WHAT   is being planned (exactly)
are the major themes
are the benefits sought
protocols or processes need to be in place
problems could arise and how serious they could be
information will be required

WHO   benefits and how
is disadvantaged and how
needs to be involved
needs to be kept informed

HOW   will the new activity affect current systems
will the new activity change relationships
will the necessary training impact on each agency
will the project end or convert to mainstream service provision

WHEN   will the new activity begin
will new protocols or processes need to be in place
will the project end or convert to mainstream service provision.

PROBLEM IDENTIFICATION

Problems can often arise as a consequence of process changes. We often call these "unintended consequences" but it is better to think of them as problems that have to be resolved. Whilst activity modelling can reduce the incidence of the unexpected, inter-disciplinary projects do not exist in a vacuum which eliminates the effects of the proclivities of personality, or system failures. Project management is not only about the application of strategic objectives to current reality, it is also about problem identification and management. Not all problems are likely to be identified in the planning process, but there are many that are to be expected and identifying them and forecasting their impact is of the essence of good project management. A simple framework for judging the seriousness of the problem and the probability that it will arise can help the project manager prioritise which problems require action and when.

There are degrees of seriousness presented by problems. Some will have more devastating effects than others, and so resolution or recovery efforts should be concentrated on problems which are most likely to frustrate the achievement of the joint initiative's objectives. Experience has shown us that problems can broadly exhibit five degrees of seriousness:

Critical problems arise from fundamental conflicts of interest or perception amongst agencies which have the potential to bring the project to a standstill;

Serious problems arise from organisational conflicts of policy or accountability which could unacceptably delay the project;

Significant problems arise from operational conflicts of procedure or method which could delay the project;

Symptomatic problems arise from the conflicts associated with the project implementation process itself (eg, staff resistance, information gaps);

Minor problems arise in the day-to-day operational phase of the project.

Problems may or may not arise, so it is important to consider the degree of probability that they will arise during the life to the project. The probability of a problem occurring is:

high   when the planned new activity is likely to become a problem very soon;

medium   when the new activity could easily become a problem in the near or medium term;

low   when the new activity may cause a problem in the medium term;

minimal   when the new activity is unlikely to cause a problem long term.

Screening problems against criteria such as these helps the project manager determine which problems require remedial attention first. It can also establish linkages between problems so that the solutions designed for one help resolve others. Above all, it helps the project manager identify solutions which do not generate further problems which themselves will require solutions!

IMPLEMENTATION

The success of any multi-disciplinary initiative is dependant on well established and easily understood and accessed lines of communication. This is most important where participants have differing traditions of professional practice and where they are based in several locations. Implementation begins before the project begins and continues throughout the life of the project.

Before the pilots begin

The project manager should facilitate a series of briefing meetings with groups of participating staff to inform them about the aim of the pilots and the benefits that multi-disciplinary working can bring to both professionals and service users. It is important to involve members of the steering group wherever possible in these briefings, and to be prepared to identify what these changes might mean in terms of changing procedures and work patterns. The meetings should be used as information gathering regarding the perspectives of the participants (see UNDERSTANDING CURRENT AND NEW ACTIVITY **Collecting information**, on page 24).

Training days for managers and supervisors should also address specific issues of processes and communication before the pilots begin. Early discussion concerning the design of the evaluation would be useful here, with key performance indicators being identified with a view to establishing the evaluation specification.

During the pilots

A programme of periodic review of progress should be established by the project manager which engages all the participants. The emphasis should be on collaboration (working together) rather than simply consultation (exchanging information). Regular but brief meetings where participants can raise issues and work on solutions to problems with each other provide the right forum for the learning that needs to take place within any multi-disciplinary initiative.

The bulk of the work in project management is in the application of broad strategic objectives to the detail of professional practice, day-to-day, and every day. Being able to address the detail and track it back to what it should mean for the broader objectives of joint working is the stuff of good project management.

Working with uncertainties will also be an everyday feature. There will be surprises, and operational problems will arise. If these difficulties did not arise, there would be little or no need for project management. Amongst the most difficult uncertainties to manage are those around personal change for participants. The feeling of loss of known work practices, and apprehension about working in unproven ways and often with different people (or with the same people in newly defined relationships) can cause participants to sink into self doubt and preoccupation with their personal futures. This can only be managed through collaboration with each agency and each participant.

WORKING WITHIN THE DEMANDS OF EVALUATION

The purpose of the evaluation is to determine the effectiveness of the project. But there is a secondary purpose which is every bit as important: the evaluation provides a discipline and a framework for managing the whole project. It provides this valuable service by:

- establishing the questions which address the effectiveness of the project;
- identifying existing data sources required to answer the questions;
- discovering the need for new data sources to provide information;
- designing information flows which keep effectiveness on the agenda of every participant.

The evaluation framework gives direction to the project, and therefore to project management activity. Working with the discipline of the evaluation in mind, the project manager assists the steering group and all the professionals involved to develop a holistic view of the project, with clear understandings of how multi-disciplinary working actually happens within a project and how it relates to the world outside the project.

CONCLUSION

The successful project manager is very much like the effective diplomat. Clarity of purpose is maintained by consistently ensuring that those involved have the right information to do what is required, and smoothing stumbling blocks in the way of new and important relationships. Continually called upon to balance the understanding of detailed operations with an anticipation of future strategic requirements, they must identify the linkages between the two. The project manager may, at times, be the only active participant in multi-disciplinary initiatives who is able to see the bigger "picture" of what services could become when health and social care professionals work in an integrated way.

JOINT ASSESSMENT AND JOINT COMMISSIONING AT THE CROSSROADS OF HEALTH AND SOCIAL CARE

INTRODUCTION

Assessment is the beginning of every health or social care intervention. Following the important and inevitable data collection in the referral processes, assessment is the first activity of the professionals involved in the purchasing or provision of care services. Whether called a screening or a primary assessment leading to what is often referred to as a "full assessment", the whole activity of determining the nature and extent of patient or client need is fundamental to identifying the level and intensity of service requirements.

Most practitioners would accept that services must be provided and monitored in relation to the needs and requirements identified in assessment. It is now considered unacceptable practice and ineffective resource management for services to be directly accessed by the service user without the benefit of a professional appraisal followed by prioritising of needs and matching of resources to those needs. But if this is true, it is astonishing that the full role assessment can play in the commissioning of services is seldom exploited. The full potential of the assessment processes remains untapped while professionals, even within the same team, carry differing and unchallenged assumptions about the meaning of assessment. By seeing assessment as only a first stage process leading to the *real* business of care provision, providers and commissioners have denied themselves the benefits that a fuller exploitation of assessment processes can yield

This paper reflects on SEIPH's experience in the development of joint assessment services for people who require both health and social care. These developments create the potential for formulating a rationale for more effective commissioning of health and social care services. Joint assessment initiatives between health and social services have concentrated on determining the needs of older people in given primary care localities. Local education authorities (LEAs) were also involved in SEIPH facilitated design of multi-disciplinary assessment of children with complex special needs.

ASSESSMENT AND JOINT ASSESSMENT

"Assessment" carries many meanings, and this is a significant problem for multi-disciplinary teams. Until there is a common understanding within the team, acceptance of assessment findings amongst professionals remains problematical. A team member with an "individual" understanding or presumption of what assessment entails runs the risk of being seen as either unskilled or over-diligent, depending on the under or over estimation of the tasks and issues involved.

There are many definitions of the assessment function within teams. Most of those currently in use can be summarised in one of these three:

> Assessment is the collecting of information from and about the applicant, reviewing that information in order to identify problems and their priority.

> Assessment is the process of helping people identify and clarify personal issues, examine their needs, circumstances and strengths in order to decide what should be done.

> Assessment is a highly participative process involving service users, carers, and other relevant people which objectively identifies needs and determines eligibility for assistance against stated criteria.

Each of these definitions taken on its own may lack some important element, but each reflects the range of assessment approaches as undertaken by a particular team. The point here is that negotiating and agreeing a common definition of assessment is fundamental to team working. The initial resistance to pinning down key concepts within teams must be skilfully managed to enable team members to agree their own definitions so that:

•   every team member knows what is expected of them as an assessor;

•   team members can question each others' assessments on the basis of this shared understanding;

•   team members can accept each others' assessments without the need to reassess.

Joint assessment takes place within multi-disciplinary teams and actively involves professionals from different agencies, traditions and structures. Authentic joint assessment is a function of these various professionals working together as a team, and where it is most effective, they work together as members of the service user's team. That is, the professionals work together and their inter-disciplinary discussions focus on the person (patient, client) rather than the processes.

Teams providing effective joint assessments are more likely to define assessment processes as:

> the recurrent activity of objectively identifying capabilities and needs with and for service users and their carers, with a view to identifying individual service plans, if necessary.

Assessment clarifies care requirements in the individual circumstances of the service user, so that agreement can be reached about what should be done, if anything.

Joint assessments can be simultaneous (two or more assessors actively engaged together with the service user) or sequential (each assessor passing on information for further assessment by a colleague). It is, of course, unlikely and probably unbearable for the service user that the whole team should assess service users' needs *en masse*. It is more likely that joint assessments will mean the blending of the sequential information and observation gathering via periodic discussions, which should involve the service user and their carers whenever possible. The essential element is that the engaging of the expertise and experience of other professionals and other relevant people becomes an indispensable part of the assessment process.

Joint assessment enjoys advantages which cannot be won by single agencies working on their own. Effective joint assessment:

- makes possible a holistic understanding of the capabilities and needs of the service user;

- empowers the service user to be involved in the planning of their care;

- provides a proper foundation for integrating and coordinating services within a single care plan;

- improves communication amongst professionals and with the service user;

- diminishes the duplication which results from agencies assessing in isolation;

• can reduce the time between initial assessment and service start date.

However, successful joint assessment initiatives are likely to have their costs. SEIPH experience shows that they are likely to require:

• the development of specific skills for multi-disciplinary working;
• shared information systems;
• locating assessors in localities close to service users (eg GP localities).

THREE MODELS OF JOINT ASSESSMENT

Three models of assessment are commonplace amongst multi-disciplinary teams, even where joint assessment is well established. These models are often unconsciously applied in what appear to be stereotypical responses to initial referrals or service requests. They are not mutually exclusive, and teams tend to estimate and manage workload by employing one or other model.

Service led assessment

This model is often employed where the initial referral requests a specific service (orange parking badges, meals services). Here the assessment can be "narrowed" because it is solely in terms of what services may be available. The assessor acts as administrator, gatekeeper and broker, with overall responsibility for rationing services efficiently to extend their availability. Little choice is offered to the applicant; the service is either available to them or, because of eligibility criteria, it is not. In that case, alternatives are usually suggested before the assessment terminates.

Needs led assessments

This is the model commonly used when initial referrals indicate complex needs which are likely to fall within the eligibility criteria of the agency. Here, assessment is in terms of the needs of service users as identified by the assessor. Needs led assessment sees the assessor acting as expert, with the authority to verify need and distribute resources for services which meet that need. The assessor often maintains responsibility for ongoing monitoring of progress under the care plan, and through this assessment process is able to offer a limited range of choice to the service user.

Choice led assessments

This model is also used in what appear to be complex cases, but here the assessment is in terms of the service user's needs <u>as identified by the service user, carers, assessors, and other relevant people.</u> Choice led assessments are not a response to the increased complexity of the case; they are a response to the professional perspective taken by the assessor. Here, the assessor acts as team facilitator, an enabler with special skills in negotiating and in influencing others. Responsibilities for resource allocation and care monitoring may still be there, but are ancillary to responsibility for assessment. This model is likely to maximize the choice available to the service user and their team.

All three models have their place in the real-world work of the team, so none should be discounted. Choice led assessment is more likely to fulfill professional and organisational ideals, but not all services users will be willing or able to participate in the fuller way of working it requires.

A NEW PROFESSIONAL PERSPECTIVE

Choice led joint assessments have the potential bo bring about a change in "culture" which most organisations will find themselves obliged to <u>allow</u>. That culture change includes the adjustment of professional perspectives graphically illustrated in figure 1. This professional "re-alignment" can be summarised in this way:

Agencies accustomed to seeing service users as entering their systems will begin to see themselves as entering the systems of service users.

The implications of this re-alignment could have profound but positive effects on the commissioning process. Most health and social care agencies currently view service users as entering their systems. Because of this perspective they tend to collect information about *their* processes - their <u>outputs</u> or activities connected with the interventions involved. Data collection is therefore likely to include:

- numbers and types of interventions;

- unit costs;

- assessment and planning events;

- staff training requirements;

-     care systems efficiency (elapsed times, waiting lists, etc).

But when agencies work together with the perspective that they are entering the systems of the service users, they create possibilities for collecting data that are more related to achievement than to processes. Whilst maintaining existing data on processes and outputs they are drawn to collecting data which is more relevant to the system of the service users, and these are inevitably about achievement and effectiveness: the <u>outcomes</u> of their work. This new approach to data collection is more likely to include evidence relating to:

-     capabilities developed or maintained;

-     diminished institutionalised behaviours;

-     social and community participation;

-     development of opportunities for improving the quality of life;

-     increased potential for employment, education or day activities.

As commissioning is theoretically based on information, a change in the type of information provided by service assessors and providers could (theoretically) change the footing of community-based health and social care commissioning. That footing is currently firmly placed in activity and event (episode) driven information. Joint assessment has the potential to enhance the language of commissioning to include issues of effectiveness as well as efficiency.

THE JOINT ASSESSMENT JIGSAW

Joint assessments present complex pictures of capabilities and needs which relate to and are influenced by personal, medical, behavioural and social circumstances. The assessment process identifies strengths as well as weaknesses, capabilities as well as needs with a view to determining a service requirement. Too often, however, professionals fall into a confusing shorthand when they describe an identified need as a service requirement. For example, it may be said that Mrs Jones needs meals on wheels, when in fact she needs appropriate nourishment and meals on wheels is only one way of ensuring that she gets it. This shows the real danger of blurring the distinctions between the assessment and the service planning phase. Busy people are, understandably, always ready to develop short-cuts to keep their workload manageable; but this is a dangerous one which threatens to obscure the distinctions between activities and achievements. In this case, the activity (output) is the provision of meals; the achievement (outcome) is a well fed Mrs. Jones!

Assessments take time and skills to piece together, but what joins together the pieces which, by themselves, represent nothing useful? What is being assessed?

Any joint health or social care assessment in the community has two axes:

*   the person;
*   the social situation.

They are in practice inseparable, making the formation of a social history which identifies significant events and relationships essential. Only for clarity are the main areas to be considered in joint assessment identified separately here.

Assessing people

It is important to assess capabilities, so the assessor is not only concerned about what people actually do, but what they can do. With this in mind, here are some of the issues which the assessor will include in evaluating current capabilities and estimating future capabilities:

self care
> perception of own capabilities
> ability to recognize and manage risk

communication
> hearing and understanding
> toleration of privacy or isolation
> ability to voice wishes, thoughts, complaints

self awareness
> self perception of abilities
> ability to link cause and effect in own behaviour

matters of personality
> emotional responses
> capacity for depression or contentment

personal behaviour
eating and sleeping
aggressiveness/passivity

special interests
use of leisure time
day activities

Assessing social situations

Any effective assessment in the community necessarily places the person in the social context which provides both the setting and the limits for their initiative and ingenuity.

Social situations present these issues for assessment:

cultural considerations
social networks
belief systems and religion
ethnic features and viewpoints

social support systems in the community
day activities
public amenities

employment and its significance
level of income
control of budgeting and spending
job stability
job satisfaction
opportunities for training and advancement

housing
appropriateness
physical environment
neighbourhood

Joint assessment practitioners working in teams have often constructed their own check lists to help them remain focussed on the issues that the team have agreed as the most important.

There is a larger "jigsaw" yet into which joint assessment must itself fit. There is a sequence of intervention which has become apparent (during the development of joint assessment initiatives) as being the most functional for the effective planning, provision and monitoring of services. This sequence is entirely dependent on assessment of individual needs, and provides three opportunities for linking commissioning processes directly with joint assessment processes. Moreover, **maintaining this sequence intact provides the foundation for commissioning services on the basis of effectiveness.**

The most effective sequence of health and social care intervention seems to be this:

1   referral and basic information collation
2   initial assessment (screening)
3   priority banding (which groups within the population is the agency designed or
     obliged to consider first)
4   joint assessment of potential service users within priority groups*
5   relating assessment outcome to service eligibility criteria
6   care planning for those who meet the service eligibility criteria*
7   negotiating for services where *service access criteria* exist
8   implementing the care plan by initiating the agreed services
9   monitoring the implementation of the care plan
10   reviewing the effectiveness of the care plan by:*
                 re-assessment
                 relating re-assessment outcome to service eligibility criteria
                 re-negotiating for services
                 implementing amended care plan.

Those indicated with an asterisk provide information most relevant to the commissioning process described later. SEIPH experience has shown that skipping stages or relaxing the sequence of the stages diminishes the effectiveness of health and social care services. The three most common "staging" problems are:

1   the application of eligibility criteria before joint assessment;
2   the confusion or lack of distinction between eligibility criteria and service access
     criteria;
3   the transition from assessment to care plan.

Maintaining the sequence intact can be a matter of slowing down the assessment processes, which often take place too rapidly. It is important to consider the distinctions between eligibility criteria and service access criteria, as well as distinguishing between assessment and care planning activities.

CLARITY ABOUT ELIGIBILITY

Eligibility criteria are simply agreed statements or descriptors which "picture" the behaviour or social circumstances of potential service users in a way which identifies the level and intensity of help, care or support they are likely to require in their everyday lives. These criteria exist to assist health and social care agencies in determining who should receive a service and at what level of intensity. Nothing more than that! The service they actually receive is a matter for service planning, which follows in sequence immediately. Eligibility criteria help translate assessment information into service planning information, and while they are guides to help professionals identify who is eligible for (should have) a service, they themselves are no guarantee of service.

There are five main benefits that eligibility criteria generate, and these are the reasons why every community health and social care agency should make them explicit:

•   assist professionals in helping the most vulnerable people in the community;

•   help focus resources on agency priorities;

•   promote consistent decision making;

•   allow needs to be prioritised and compared with the total local demand for service;

•   promote realism by informing the public about agency priorities and capabilities.

Eligibility criteria are often confused with priority groups, which are simply the of groups within the population sharing similar characteristics which an agency agrees or accepts as being likely to be most in need of its services. Priority groups identify people, not their eligibility for services. Here are some examples of priority groups:

        people who are registered blind or partially sighted;
        people with mobility problems;
        people with chronic physical disabilities;

people with learning disabilities;
people with a mental health diagnosis;
people between 16-65 years of age.

SEIPH has found the general lack of a distinction made amongst professionals between eligibility criteria and service access criteria to be a major problem. Service access criteria are service provider generated statements which identify the characteristics of services users who are most likely to benefit from a particular service. Eligibility criteria identify the people who should receive a service, while service access criteria identify people who are likely to benefit from a particular service, which may or may not take its place in the care plan.

Many services are specialized, designed to meet the needs of particular groups of people, all of whom may be eligible for a service. In many cases professionals must ration (prioritise) their services to those who can benefit most, and this means excluding others even though their needs may have satisfied existing eligibility criteria. A service user can be eligible for a service yet fail to satisfy the criteria for a particular service. Service access criteria help service providers draw the line between those who will receive their services and those who will not. This does not affect eligibility, but it does delay the implementation of the care plan as alternatives must be sought.

Here are some examples of service access criteria:

service users must be under 75 years of age;
service users must have a physical disability;
service users must have moderate learning disabilities but no physical disabilities;
service users must live within two miles of this facility.

Confusion about these important and fundamental concepts can only amplify confusion where it already exists in professional practice, resulting in a disruption to the essential sequence for linking joint assessment with commissioning.

TRANSLATING ASSESSMENTS INTO CARE PLANS

Care plans are "fudged" by well intentioned assessors who fail to distinguish the assessment from the care planning stage. Service led and needs led assessments are easily and commonly biased by the assessor's presumption of what resources are likely to be available. A choice led assessment is less likely to be biased because its processes <u>include</u> people, with the assessor primarily acting as a facilitator of discussion and choice.

SEIPH has found that even where assessment processes are kept distinct from care planning there is often a gulf (something of a Bermuda Triangle) between many joint assessments and the care plan which follows. Care planning in these cases seems to be anchored to the availability of existing resources rather than to the conclusions drawn as a result of assessment. Service users whose needs can only be met by a service requiring unusual or atypical arrangements will lose out because professionals assume that service users will (and should!) be prepared to be more flexible than the services provided. When comparing cases which demonstrate a broad range of good quality joint assessments of people with diverse and complex special needs, it is alarming to discover a great similarity in the content of the care plans which follow assessment.

Joint assessment and care management are founded on the principle that services should be flexible and accessible enough to meet the needs of the service user. The simple guideline is this:

Fit the services to the person, not the person into the services!

SEIPH has established five points to consider when converting assessment information into care plans. They aim to provide the professional with practical guidance during this crucial step.

Stay at the margins

Staying marginal simply means that the service user (and not the professional) is at the centre of the process. The assessor must find the balance between participating and observing. Becoming over or under-involved means losing the balance of objectivity. Maintaining this balance helps avoid being diverted to assessing only some needs (those for which services are available) while ignoring others. It also saves the professional from becoming a permanent part of the service user's care solution!

Be specific

Joint assessments will be full of information, so do not settle for plans based on summaries. Specifically link identified need with a service requirement, and then see how that requirement could be fulfilled. Existing services may be appropriate, but some requirements may necessitate special arrangements. Identified needs resulting in service requirements which cannot be met even though alternatives have been explored become "unmet needs" and must be recorded as such.

Forget "packages of care"

Care plans should be offering more than bundles of services or activities. Service users do not consider "care packaging" to be an attractive concept, as it has "off the peg" connotations and is therefore, unsuited to their needs. A much more positive approach is needed where care planning is also offering a progression of opportunities for maintaining or increasing personal capabilities.

Design the care plan with others

This is a joint task, so encourage the service user to do as much as possible. Address identified needs, but focus on choice and negotiate toward an agreed service requirement. Take care to ensure that the service user has the ability to benefit from the service requirement of choice. Prioritise needs (safety first, etc.) and service requirements (what needs to happen before other needs can be met), and identify risks which can be managed by the service user themselves.

Review the plan

Care plans are often neglected once implemented. It is essential that they are reviewed when the service user needs, whether or not they request it. Statutory requirements are useful but may not meet the needs of the service user. During the review it is *essential* to review the original assessment as well as the care plan. Again, identify need but concentrate on choice.

JOINT ASSESSMENT AND CARE PLANNING: THE FOUNDATION OF JOINT COMMISSIONING

Joint assessment is at the centre of what has proven to be an expanding picture of how health and social care professionals intervene with service users and interact with each other. This bigger picture is the everyday stuff of service provision, and has the potential for providing information at the joint assessment, care planning and review stages that could change the language of commissioning.

Currently joint commissioning is relatively rare. Sometimes 'joint commissioning' refers to what are in fact rather complex systems for negotiating cost-sharing in a number of highly complex cases <u>after care plans have been devised</u>. Authentic joint commissioning begins at the early stages of joint assessment, and requires agencies to agree policies, strategies and procedures which facilitate the joint provision of health and social care services (and education services when children are involved) <u>to the same people</u>. Ideally this means developing:

- agreements about priority groups to be served;

- shared or congruent information systems;

- single referral point mechanisms for accessing both health and social care;

- common assessment policies and procedures;

- agreements relating to finance and funding conventions;
- methods of monitoring the effectiveness of the care purchased through the commissioning processes.

If practical and easy to use methodologies can be developed to identify effective health and social care, commissioning processes can begin to focus on proven effectiveness rather than on contacts, episodes or events.

Looking at the nature of contracting can give some clues as to how such a practical approach to determining the effectiveness of health and social care service can be constructed. Current thinking could offer this modest definition:

> Joint commissioning is the activity of health and social care agencies working together to identify what needs exist, to specify services which meet those needs, and to contract with provider agencies to ensure that those services are provided.

This definition is both modest and incomplete. Health and social care commissioners have another responsibility to ensure that the services provided are effective. The fact that a service is provided says nothing about its effectiveness; it merely confirms its existence! The definition of contracting can be improved by reflecting on the ten stages of intervention described previously on page 38.

Three stages of the sequence are points when the information required for effective commissioning is at hand:

Stage 4   joint assessment of potential service users within priority groups
Stage 6   care planning for those who meet the service eligibility criteria
Stage 10 reviewing the effectiveness of the care plan

These stages associated with joint assessment are able to provide information required for more effective commissioning:

*   about needs;
*   about services;
*   about the effectiveness of services for meeting needs.

Now joint commissioning can be defined in terms which refocus its processes on effectiveness. The simple definition of joint commissioning has been enhanced:

> **Joint commissioning is the activity of health and social care agencies working together to identify needs, specify services which meet those needs, and contract with providers for selected services which are known to be effective in meeting those needs.**

Rather than simply purchasing service events or episodes, commissioners will be able to selectively purchase services with proven effectiveness. Measuring the effectiveness of community based health and social care has been an illusory ideal for social care agencies, yet many of them contain all the information required to do it; they only lack a simple methodology to access that information.

MEASURING EFFECTIVENESS BY MONITORING SERVICE OUTCOMES

Five years at the crossroads of health and social care have convinced SEIPH of the need for simple to use methods of monitoring effectiveness in community care. SEIPH is currently piloting a system involving the collection of data at stages 4, 6 and 10 in the sequence outlined earlier. The core data, therefore, are already contained within the agencies' case records. The methodology is designed to build on assessment systems already in place and does not add significantly to professionals' workload. No additional case reviews are required and random case audits, though desirable, are not essential. The data collected eventually expand to become information which both commissioners and providers of care can use to inform the commissioning and contracting processes more realistically.

The rationale for the whole of SEIPH's effectiveness measuring model is examined fully in SEIPH's publication *"Q-Trek: The Pursuit of Quality"*, published in 1996. Briefly, the model involves five steps:

Step 1 Ensuring that all participating professionals understand the difference between service outputs and service outcomes
outputs are activities: outcomes are the effects of those activities.

Step 2 Identifying typical service outcomes to be monitored
Commissioners, Purchasers and service provision professionals work together, to identify the outcomes (achievements) they commonly work towards with service users in a particular priority group. Service users and carers could also be involved.
It is important that the outcomes are:

> negotiated and agreed by all involved;
> realistic and achievable.

Step 3 Coding the chosen outcomes

This is a simple process which adapts the identified outcomes to a spreadsheet or database format. The advantage of a database system is that it can collect outcome data in coded form so that the information can be easily aggregated and interrogated.

Outcomes may or may not be achieved (or partially achieved) for a variety of reasons. Reasons for achievement, non-achievement or partial achievement are also agreed and coded.

Step 4 Recording codes onto database (spreadsheet)

Recording of codes happens at the time of care planning and review. During review, determinations are made about whether the outcome:
> was achieved
> was partially achieved
> was not achieved

within the time targets of the care plan. Codes identifying achievement, non-achievement or partial achievement are also recorded during the review process.

Unless the service terminates, new outcomes are then identified as targets to be monitored by a subsequent review.

Step 5   Interrogating and interpreting outcome measurement data

Once sufficient information from the assessment, care planning and review stages is input on the database, it can be easily interpreted by outcome code, achievement/non-achievement code or time targets. Commissioners will then be able to identify:

- the outcomes achieved by (the effectiveness of) the service;

- reasons why the service has proven effective;

- the percentage of outcomes achieved within the time target;

- the outcomes not achieved by the service and reasons why;

- which services are more successful at achieving particular outcomes; and which services are under-achieving and why.

CONCLUSION

Assessment is both the beginning and the foundation of effective health and social care. Joint assessment provides the opportunity for developing new perspectives about the understanding of the capability and needs of service users. Properly done, joint assessments can become the basis of collaborative planning where service effectiveness as well as service activity can be monitored. Planning services when information about effectiveness exists begins the move away from activity or event-based commissioning and opens the door to developing services on the basis of their effectiveness.

EVALUATION DESIGN AND ACTION RESEARCH

INTRODUCTION

This paper addresses the question of how to evaluate multi-agency projects using an action research approach. The first section explains what evaluation is; how it differs from monitoring, in that it is essentially a research process; and how an action research approach lends itself to the sort of multi-agency developmental projects to be evaluated. The second section explains in ten steps how to design an action research evaluation. The third and final section highlights some further issues to be aware of when designing an evaluation: these are set out as "top tips".

It is not intended to discuss here the methodological underpinnings of action research, nor is it possible in a paper of this length to describe in detail the methods that might be used. (Some examples of research instruments developed for use in SEIPH projects are included, however, in the paper on **INFORMATION SYSTEMS AND DATA COLLECTION.**) Evaluation is a research task, demanding research knowledge and skills: these will need to be accessed either from within one or more of the participating agencies, or by commissioning an organisation or individual external to the project. However, action research depends on widespread awareness of and participation in the research process by everyone involved in the project. It is not a "hands off" approach, and the more understanding everyone has of the task of designing, carrying out and using the evaluation, the better will be the overall impact on the development of the project.

The aim of this paper then, is to familiarise people with the evaluation process and enable them each to play their part more confidently and creatively, developing useful research skills along the way and contributing to the further improvement of the project in which they are involved.

WHAT IS EVALUATION AND WHAT IS ACTION RESEARCH?

Evaluation is a process of finding out how well a project or a service is working. To what extent is it meeting its overall aims? Is it meeting all of the specific objectives set for it? *Informal evaluation* happens all the time, as people involved in the project observe and experience what is going on, identify problems and seek solutions together. By the end of the project everyone involved has a strong sense of how well it has worked and some idea as to which aspects worked better than others and why. Usually there will have been some debate during the course of a project as to how best to proceed and different people may have expressed differing or even opposing views about this. The steering group may have had a difficult task at times to keep the project on course, helped by the skills of a project manager, but almost certainly everyone will have learnt a great deal about the process. They will also have some idea of what the outcomes have been, and whether they have been good enough to justify extending new ways of working more widely.

So why carry out a *formal evaluation*? There are three main reasons:

- to demonstrate in a <u>systematic and clearly recorded</u> way the extent of the project's success and the lessons learnt, for the benefit of all who took part ;

- to reflect the full range of views about the project from the perspectives of all the different stakeholders (service users, carers, different professional groups and different organisations);

- to inform decision-making about future policy and practice.

Sometimes there is confusion about the terms 'monitoring' and 'evaluation.' Essentially, monitoring answers the question "what is happening?" while evaluation asks "how well is it happening?" Monitoring is clearly an important component of evaluation, but it is rather limited without the next step, which seeks to explore what is going on behind the linear trends and patterns identified by monitoring. Information systems in organisations are often designed to monitor trends in volume of service delivery, caseload or spend, for example. Such systems, if they are well designed, properly used and regularly quality-tested, give a systematic and rigorous approach to data collection. Evaluation seeks to *interrogate the data,* on the basis of a research question such as "How and why does caseload vary across different client groups?"

Formal evaluation is a particular type of research activity, demanding the application of research skills, knowledge and techniques. Research can be simply defined as a <u>systematic and carefully documented process of finding out</u>. Within this overall definition, however, there is a broad spectrum of activity, ranging from rigorous academic research studies, in which aims, methods, results and conclusions are presented in a highly structured way, to more pragmatic "here and now" approaches which aim to improve services in an incremental way learning as we go rather than to prove the case once and for all. Different approaches to research in general, and to evaluation in particular, call for different designs and lead to different levels of generalisability. Provided everyone is aware of this, there should not be a problem.

So what is *action research*?

Action research is an approach to research design which has been described as "using research to study and change something you care about" (Loraine Blaxter et al. *How to Research* Open University Press). In an action research project, development and evaluation go hand in hand, each feeding the other along the way. This is very different from the idea that evaluation should be detached from and "uncontaminated" by developments in the project (and vice versa).

In designing an evaluation programme for projects set up to explore new ways of working to deliver services more effectively, the use of action research is a creative response to the problem of constantly changing parameters. It recognises that what is being researched is liable to change during the course of the research. This can happen as a result of the research process itself: for example, people who are interviewed about their expectations of a new service are likely to think differently about their role than if they had not been asked. Or it may be as a result of events outside the evaluation, for example, reorganisation of one of the agencies involved may lead to a change of working practice or procedures during the course of the evaluation. The action research approach also recognises that people who are developing new ways of working in complex organisations do not want to wait three years for the results of an evaluation: project managers want to know what is happening while it is happening so that they can do something about it, and steering groups want information to inform decision making in their organisations now. Politics won't wait. Evaluations based on action research are therefore, by necessity and by design, more focussed on *improving the service* than on *proving the case.*

DESIGNING AN EVALUATION USING ACTION RESEARCH

An action research evaluation requires a design that is flexible and responsive, but it also requires a research attitude which is both rigorous and creative. Interestingly, this approach to evaluation reflects the type of service approaches that are being introduced through the joint working projects that are being evaluated: holistic, responsive to individual needs and preferences, open to learning from experience and willing to modify as necessary, flexible enough to respond to varied and changing needs, and so on. There is a built-in recognition in this type of evaluation that there is not "one best way", but rather that different benefits may be identified for different stakeholders. Service users, carers, different staff groups, managers and organisations all stand to gain and lose in different ways. What is good for one may not be so for another. That is why it is so important to take all perspectives into account, rather than seeking for one objective right answer.

A STEP BY STEP GUIDE TO EVALUATION DESIGN

1. Identify the *research question* which will underpin the evaluation.

2. Break down the overall research question into specific *criteria for measuring the success* of the project; make sure these match the *project's objectives.*

3. Decide what the principal components of the evaluation are; make sure they reflect all the *stakeholders'* perspectives.

4. Identify what *resources* are available and what the *timescale* is.

5. Begin to map out a *programme* of evaluation which includes all the components and reflects available resources and timescale considerations.

6. Decide what *data* are required to answer the questions about each component, and choose the most appropriate *methods* for collecting the data.

7. Think about how the data will be *analysed.*

8. Consider how the results will be *interpreted.*

9. Decide how the findings will be *reported.*

10. Decide how the results of the evaluation will be *presented, shared, and used.*

The process of designing the evaluation, from the first step of deciding on the research question to the final step of deciding how results will be presented, shared and used, is a task for the steering group. The process needs to be facilitated by someone with research skills, and this will preferably be the researcher who is coordinating the evaluation. In an action research evaluation, the project manager has a key role in mediating the process, to check that the evaluation will properly inform project development throughout the lifetime of the project. The task of ensuring that the evaluation findings are fed into mainstream developments beyond the lifetime of the project is once again down to the steering group.

STEP 1   Identify the *research question* which will underpin the evaluation

The key concerns expressed by the steering group need to be transformed into a clearly defined and researchable question, ie a question that can be answered using appropriate research methods. The research question will later be broken down to generate a more specific list of questions to be researched, and each of these in turn will generate the sort of questions to be included in questionnaires, focus group topic guides or interview schedules, depending on the methods used.

The starting point is for the steering group to answer, in one short sentence, the deceptively simple question "why do we want to evaluate this project?". There may be many reasons for carrying out an evaluation and they will determine the overall shape or design of the evaluation. In multi-agency projects, each organisation's agenda will influence the perceived reason for carrying out an evaluation. Different perspectives will need to be taken into account to decide what the areas of agreement are. It is important therefore to focus the discussion initially on what the overall purpose of the evaluation is, rather than allowing debate to begin immediately as to the specific elements that require evaluation, what outcomes are being sought and so on. Simply deciding upon one straightforward and unambiguous question is difficult enough and is all that is required for this first step.

Answers to the opening question "why do we want to evaluate this project?" might be on the lines of:

> "We want to know if this particular model of joint working works"

OR   "We want to know whether to extend this pilot project across the locality/borough"

OR   " We want to know which model works better"

These responses are similar but different, and it is important to know which one is of paramount importance. Steering group members often want to include more than one central question, but this should be avoided as far as possible because it increases the risk that the evaluation will lose focus. Furthermore, having decided on the overall question which should in turn reflect the overall aim or purpose of the project it is important to stick with it throughout the duration of the project.

STEP 2.   Break down the overall research question into specific *criteria for measuring the success* of the project; make sure these match the *project's objectives*

When the group has agreed what the overall purpose of the evaluation is, the researcher can then probe for clarity and definition, asking, for example "what do you mean by 'the model works' or 'the model works better'?" This will prompt discussion about what the agreed criteria of success are.

The criteria for success should of course be the same as the objectives of the project. Ideally, the project will have been designed with the evaluation design built in from the very beginning. This entails having research skills as well as project management skills on hand to enable the steering group to develop a set of clearly defined, achievable, and measurable objectives. The process of developing the research question on which to base the evaluation will have already been an integral part of developing the project. In practice, however, this is not always the case. More often, and for understandable reasons, all the initial energy and thinking is put into getting the project up and running. Objectives are set which may reflect the composite views of the steering group, but which do not necessarily permit systematic and rigorous investigation using the battery of research techniques.

To be most effective, an action research evaluation needs to be firmly embedded in the "think tank" phase of the steering group's life, right at the beginning.

STEP 3   Decide what the principal components of the evaluation are; make sure they reflect all the *stakeholders'* perspectives

Having focussed in on one overall aim or purpose (Step 1) and then broken this down into several criteria for measuring success against objectives (Step 2), it is now time to consider what might be included in the evaluation, bearing in mind the need to reflect the perspectives of all the *stakeholders*, in other words all the groups who might have an interest in the project, including service users and carers, professional staff, managers, local authority members, and so on . If you have not already done so, you will first need to identify a list of stakeholders that is appropriate for your own project. The accompanying paper THE ROLE OF THE MULTI-AGENCY STEERING GROUP includes a list of potential organisations, statutory, voluntary and community groups, who might represent the various stakeholders: this is a starting point.   Having identified the stakeholders, the task of deciding what the principal components of the evaluation might be can perhaps best be tackled by brainstorming. Ideally this should be done by the steering group, with the aim of listing as many things as possible that different groups might want to know about the success or otherwise of the project. Think of all the anticipated benefits (for example: "better communication within the primary care team", "better information for carers about what's going on", "improved access for black people"), and then all the possible obstacles to achieving these (such as "GPs won't have time to be involved"; "organisational change in the agencies is on the horizon again"). If all the stakeholders are represented on the steering group already, this task is made easier although it may take longer! If, however, not all the stakeholders are represented, you will need to decide how to check out their views, to ensure that they are not being misrepresented or ignored altogether.

Having produced a list of twenty or thirty items in this way, it is then useful to set them against one or more checklists to make sure that the evaluation is both rounded and well balanced, in other words checking that it takes all aspects and perspectives into account and does not emphasise one element or perspective at the expense of others. Some of the checklists that are most useful are set out in the accompanying paper on THE ROLE OF THE MULTI-AGENCY STEERING GROUP: these include the boxes on empowerment, equality, quality, and stakeholders.

STEP 4.   Identify what *resources* are available and what the *timescale* is

Resources: Those that might be made available for the evaluation include people, research skills, knowledge, and money. If a specific budget has been set for the evaluation, this will determine the scope of the work to some extent, but there may be opportunities to enhance the overall resourcing of the research, by tapping the interest of professional staff involved in the project, for example, and by prudent use of external researchers. Now is the time to be both realistic and opportunistic about resources: almost certainly there will not be enough to do all you would like to do with the multi-dimensional set of components in step 3. Scaling down may involve selecting some core components that can reasonably be expected to come within the set budget, and then allowing for additional components to be tackled if and when resources can be identified.

Timescale: When are the results needed? For example, are policy decisions about extending the life of the project to be made part way through? Or is this a demonstration project upon which a roll-out programme to mainstream service provision is to be based, depending on decisions to be made before the project has run its course? Can these requirements be met by preparing interim reports of findings, in addition to the ongoing feedback to the project manager and steering group?

STEP 5.   **Begin to map out a *programme* of evaluation which includes all the components and reflects available resources and timescale considerations**

This step involves deciding on the overall shape of the evaluation. You may decide, for example, that the evaluation will take the form of a fairly straightforward "before" and "after" appraisal, based on monitoring referrals over the duration of the project to track response times and gathering feedback from service users, staff and managers at the beginning and end of the project (or at regular intervals during the project). Or you may decide that the evaluation will need to take place in two or three phases or stages to match the phased implementation of the project, and that different components will be evaluated at different stages.

Whatever the overall shape, deciding upon it will help to determine a schedule of events, what you want to know and when. You will then be able to adjust the schedule to allow for resource availability. For example, if you have a consistent amount of data collection time available throughout the duration of the project, you will need to gather feedback from different groups at different times (eg. service user feedback in months 1, 7 and 13; staff feedback in months 2, 8 and 14).

Although you will probably already have some idea of how you will go about collecting the various data, designing an overall programme comes before deciding on data collection methods. It is important to keep something of an open mind as to methods while you are still thinking broadly about "what do we want to know and when?". Subsequently, however, you will need to go back and forth between steps 5, 6 and 7 to come up with a complete evaluation plan that encompasses design, method and analysis, in other words how the evaluation research will be carried out.

STEP 6.   **Decide what *data* are required to answer the questions about each component, and choose the most appropriate *methods* for collecting the data**

Action research is essentially a *qualitative* approach, and uses predominantly although not exclusively qualitative methods, such as in depth interviews, focus groups, documentary analysis and observation. However, it will generally include a quantitative component based on monitoring systems, for example to track referrals and analyse response times, or to monitor spend. (Setting up tracking systems is discussed in the accompanying paper on **INFORMATION SYSTEMS AND DATA COLLECTION**.) Having quantitative data to analyse is useful for answering specific "what is happening?" type questions: Are inappropriate referrals happening more or less often over time? Do they happen more frequently in this model than in that model?, and so on. A qualitative approach asks the question "what is happening?" in a more general way, leaving the way open for new insights into what is going on, and where possible why and how it might be changed.

Some of the main qualitative methods that may be used are set out in box 4.1. When you have some idea of the methods that might work best for the questions you are seeking to answer, you will need to check that the resources are there, both in terms of people and skills to tackle the various methods (back to step 4) and in terms of the amount of time, skills and equipment required to analyse the data generated by different methods (forward to step 7, and then back to step 4, and so on!).

Gradually you will be able to fit the methods you have chosen into the overall programme which had begun to take shape in step 5. You will be in a position to map out the evaluation design in detail, with the order and timescale of events clearly shown, and ideally demonstrated in diagrammatic form such as a chart or grid. Different methods may appear either *in series* (ie where one follows the next, for example the results of a focus group might be used to identify the more detailed questions to be included in a set of in-depth interviews); or *in parallel* (ie more than one method being used simultaneously, for example a set of interviews with primary care team members is conducted at the same time as a postal survey of managers).

STEP 7.   Think ahead about how the data will be *analysed*

There are important timescale considerations here. It is important to remember, for example, that analysing qualitative material such as focus group tapes or notes from telephone interviews is extremely time-consuming. There is no economy of scale in analysis: twenty interviews take twice as long to analyse as ten, and a two-hour focus group for six to eight people can take as long as six or eight individual interviews. The trick is to limit the number of interviews to a manageable number, bearing in mind the need to achieve a certain level of coverage and range. For example, you might decide to interview just two staff from each discipline, or to hold four focus groups for users in four different age groups. Quality and richness of data are what matter in this kind of research, not quantity or representative sampling. It is much better to conduct and analyse a few interviews, or analyse a few case note files carefully and thoroughly than to skim over a larger number.

STEP 8   Consider how the results will be *interpreted*

Action research calls for interactive methods, so that participants have the opportunity to give feedback on the findings ("This is what we've found so far. Have we got it right?") before taking them on board and deciding where to go next. The roles of project manager and steering group in articulating this part of the process are crucial in ensuring a comprehensive and balanced view of the findings and a steady move forward.

STEP 9   Decide how the findings will be *reported*

How fully will results be reported? How will difficult or unwelcome findings be dealt with? The role of the researcher can be compromised here, and to avoid this requires a careful balancing act on the part of the steering group, between the steering group deciding what is to be included and what is not on the one hand, and respecting the independence of the researcher on the other. This issue needs sensitive handling whether the evaluation is being coordinated by an in-house researcher or an external researcher or researchers.

STEP 10   Decide how the results of the evaluation will be *presented, shared, and used*

Turning the outputs of the evaluation (interim and final reports, for example) into user-friendly materials and, ultimately, outcomes is the final creative step. Poster displays, newsletters, seminars, workshops and conferences are some of the most widely used ways of sharing the findings of an evaluation. Choose ways of doing this that are as energising as possible, to keep the enthusiasm and therefore the momentum high as the project draws to a close, so that the ideas behind it and the debate generated by the research and development process are kept alive.

AND FINALLY... DON'T FORGET TO CELEBRATE!

Planning ahead for a final celebration is a good way of building in success from the beginning. You don't even have to wait for the end: celebrations are a good way of maintaining momentum during the life of the project. One ambitious and complex multi-agency project, for example, involving dozens of staff and managers and spread over several primary care practices, held a "Celebration Lunch" at the beginning of a new phase of the project. This was well attended, enjoyable and prompted the chair of the steering group to comment that he was astonished just how many people in different organisations were involved in making the project work.

Box : 4.1   Qualitative methods used in evaluating multi-agency projects

- **Observation**
  Participant or non-participant? (or somewhere in between?)

- **Document analysis**
  eg analysis of a year's steering group minutes against a checklist of questions;
  analysis of a sample of joint assessments undertaken during the first and final
  quarters of the project's time span.

- **Questionnaire (survey)**
  By post, or handed out at the surgery, for example? Surveys are usually described
  as a quantitative method, but can be used in a qualitative way, with questionnaires
  comprising some closed, coded "tick-box" *quantifiable* elements and some space
  for open responses.

- **Interview**
  Face-to-face or telephone? Structured or semi-structured interview schedules?
  NB: at the end of interview schedules it is helpful to leave space for the
  interviewer's comments and observations. These spontaneous notes capture the
  interviewer's initial overall impression and can give a useful insight which is
  otherwise lost.

- **Focus groups**
  A focus group is essentially a group interview, run as a facilitated discussion with
  about half a dozen questions used as a *topic guide* to promote discussion among a
  small group (five to eight is ideal) of people who do not know each other but have
  in common an interest in the subject being discussed. For example, they may all be
  patients of a particular practice, or of a similar age-group and/or ethnic background.
  The discussion is taped and analysed to identify the range and predominance of
  themes emerging. (NB: Where groups of people know each other for example the
  community nurses of the locality in question - a true focus group is not possible,
  because of the existing group dynamic, but facilitated discussion can still be a
  useful source of data.)

- **Keeping a Diary**
  These can be very useful in an action research project, both in showing how the
  project has developed over time - possibly from a number of different perspectives -
  and also in acting as an ongoing reminder to those who are keeping a diary of how
  things seemed previously and how things might have changed. Decide who might
  keep a diary, eg the researcher, project manager, professional staff, support staff,
  service users, carers, steering group members; also what sort of information might
  be recorded, and how often. As with all forms of data collection that depend on
  individual record keeping, remember to check regularly that people are filling them
  in, and are sure of how and why they are doing this.

FURTHER ISSUES

While the evaluation process can be thought of as a series of steps, all of which need to be thought through at the design stage, there are a number of further considerations which should be kept in mind during the design, carrying out and completion of any evaluation. In evaluating multi-agency projects some of these issues are more complex than usual, but they do not need to be over complicated. They are set out here as "top tips".

TOP TIPS for SUCCESSFUL EVALUATION

- **Keep everyone informed**

- **Ethics matter!**

- **Equality is vital**

- **Choose pilot areas carefully**

- **Use external researchers wisely**

- **Evaluate for success**

- **Be flexible and open to learning as you go**

- **Be rigorous and creative - know when to compromise and when not to**

Keep everyone informed

Keeping everyone informed from the very beginning about the project, the evaluation and the use of action research pays enormous dividends. A useful way of doing this is to design a briefing sheet (two sides of A4 paper will be enough) and to arrange to have large numbers of copies well produced on good quality and eye-catching paper (making sure that the inevitable bootlegged photocopies will reproduce clearly). A well produced briefing sheet legitimises the project as well as giving people a chance to become involved in some way, and is useful preparation for the eventual widening out of the project into mainstream activity. Designing the sheet in question and answer fashion works well ("What is the project?", "How did it come about?", "How will it work?", and so on). Don't worry if not all the answers are obvious at this stage. It is acceptable to say that the project is experimenting with new ways of working without giving details of operational guidelines that have still to be developed. What is important is to get this basic information out <u>early</u> and distribute it <u>widely</u>. In most areas undertaking joint agency projects, there are likely to be literally hundreds if not thousands of people who potentially "need to know" about the project. It is in everyone's interests to make sure that what they know is timely, accurate and easy to read.

Ethics matter!

Think this through from the start. For example, you may need to seek NHS ethical approval from your local Research Ethics Committee if you want to include patients directly in your research. The question of how you will gain patients' consent, for example, will need to be considered, as will issues of confidentiality and anonymity: under what circumstances will confidentiality be broken, for example in cases of disclosure of abuse or neglect of children or elders. Anti-discrimination is also called for on ethical grounds.

The overarching rule is "do no harm". In practice this may mean compromising the richness of results so as to minimise the risk of adverse effects on participants. This includes everyone who may be involved professionally in the project, as well as service users and carers. Staff who are being interviewed, for example, should be protected from the risk that any adverse comments they may make will be attributed to them and lead to blame or complaint. This needs careful thinking through, because often in small, local projects it is almost impossible to report people's views anonymously, without it being possible for those involved in the project to narrow down their identity to one or two. If necessary, compromises must be made, even if this means deciding not to report some findings. However, it is important to acknowledge that even when all steps to protect people have been taken, there is still some risk. It is impossible to legislate against the unethical behaviour of others, for example.

Equality is vital

There is a wealth of research evidence to show clearly that people's experiences of health and social care services can vary quite widely according to age, ethnic and cultural background, gender, sexual orientation, and socio-economic situation. Yet all too often these factors are not fully taken into account in designing research and development projects which explore new ways of working. If equal opportunities are to be made real, we need to know whether joint working makes services more accessible to all groups, for example, and how new ways of working address old problems of unequal access. Evaluation needs to take account of everyone's perspective, and to pay special attention to groups who may be at risk of being marginalised or excluded both in practice and in our thinking. Make sure that minority ethnic groups, people in residential care, homeless people and people with multiple disabilities, for example, are included. Design a checklist to ensure that everyone is included in the evaluation, by listing the answers to the following questions: Who is out there? How might taking them into account influence the evaluation at each stage? How might they be involved at each stage of the evaluation?

Choose pilot areas carefully

The selection of pilot sites is often done before the question of evaluation is even considered, yet the choice of sites has important implications for the evaluation. Criteria might include the likely chances of success; the willingness and interest of a particular team or practice; the availability of spare offices to accommodate care managers, and so on. These criteria may take precedence in practice over theoretical considerations such as the geographical and socio-economic variation across the district or the spread of single-handed and group practices. There may be some inherent bias in the selection process, and it is as well to be explicit about this from the beginning, and to be aware of the implications for the generalisability of evaluation results.

Use external researchers wisely

The question of whether and when to use external researchers is an important one. It is unlikely that all the necessary skills and resources will be available in-house, but that does not mean that the whole evaluation exercise should be handed over to external researchers. Depending on the level of resources available, external research support may be brought in to assist with the evaluation design, to do part or all of the data collection, and to write up the findings and report them to the project manager or direct to the project teams and steering group. Alternatively, external research support may be used to supervise an in-house researcher. However the evaluation is carried out, the steering group will have a key role in the evaluation. Whatever the extent of external research support, the external researcher will always be working alongside the in-house steering group and project manager.

Evaluate for success

Sometimes people are so tied to the idea that research must endeavour to be objective that they believe that the aim of an evaluation is to "tell it as it is, warts and all". While there is some truth in this and it is certainly not useful to deny or hide unwelcome findings revealed during the course of the research it is helpful to remember that the aim of evaluating multi-agency projects is to *improve joint working for the benefit of everyone involved.* A positive approach to evaluation will help this process. Good outcomes are worth highlighting and celebrating. Poor outcomes are to be acknowledged and learnt from but do not need over-emphasising. The notion of evaluating for success should be tackled openly by the steering group at the beginning: if one or two members do not trust the process, they may be inclined to sabotage success in the name of objectivity and balance. Reassuring them that the intention is to promote good practice and learn from mistakes will hopefully avoid the problem.

Be flexible and open to learning as you go

This means being prepared to keep the evaluation design under review and modify it if necessary. Steering group members do not always welcome this idea, because they understandably want to get on with the operational tasks of the project. Yet from experience it is clear that it is only by being prepared to keep the evaluation process on the agenda - rather than setting it up and waiting for the results - that the whole research and development process is kept on course. This may include a review and reworking of the project's objectives, which is a constructive response to development. In action research, it is only the overall purpose of the project or evaluation that is sacrosanct and not subject to change. Everything else is open to review and modification taking into account the impact that change in direction will have on the final outcomes.

Be rigorous and creative - know when to compromise and when not to

This is a difficult balance to achieve, after all this is *research* we're doing and it must conform to the basic requirements of systematic and rigorous enquiry. Nonetheless in action research the inevitable messiness ("complexity" doesn't even get close to describing it!) is acceptable, and compromises are sometimes necessary. What is important is to describe what has been done, and how and why, in reporting findings.

INFORMATION SYSTEMS AND
DATA COLLECTION

INTRODUCTION

This paper looks at how to use existing information systems and also how to set up specific systems to collect the data required to support the research and development process in multi-agency projects. It is based on the experience gained in a number of such projects, managed and evaluated by SEIPH.

The first section explores the role of in-house information systems in ongoing monitoring of the business processes of the organisations likely to take part in multi-agency projects. The second section examines the potential role of existing information systems in providing evaluation data for joint projects. The third section describes how specially designed systems both manual and computerised can be used to supplement or replace mainstream information systems to provide evaluation data for such projects.

INFORMATION SYSTEMS AND THEIR ROLE IN ONGOING MONITORING

"Everywhere there are data management systems masquerading as information systems"
(anon.)

All information systems are designed with one overall purpose: to provide information. Yet most of the in-house information systems developed to monitor community care, such as assessment and care planning, are not really providing useful information, either for managers or operational staff. What they provide are masses of data. Converting raw data into useful information depends on good business analysis by the IT department working in conjunction with managers and front-line staff to ensure that the potential of the system to convert data into useful information is maximised.

The quality of information also depends on the quality of data. This is such a well known fact that it should not need restating, but it does need restating, for the simple reason that, in many organisations, poor quality of data input is still leading to poor data output and less than useful information. Poor quality input most often has to do with work overload on professional and support staff, rather than poor systems design. The second most frequently cited reason is that there are not enough terminals available: this can be exacerbated by requirements that, for example, essential assessment data must be logged within a certain number of hours of carrying out the assessment. Meeting the quality standard of speedy recording may compromise the quality of the data for all but the most immediate purposes.

Information systems managers usually express concern over the quality of client data, whilst financial data are much more reliable. There is an inherent logic in this. If the details of service delivery orders are not accurately or fully recorded, the service may not be delivered, or may be seriously delayed. If, on the other hand, client details are inaccurately or incompletely loaded onto the computer, this is unlikely to impact on immediate service outcomes. However, this gap of course severely limits the use of aggregate data for planning purposes, and is also likely to impede the review process for the individual.

JOINT INFORMATION SYSTEMS: AN ESSENTIAL ILLUSION?

It is a paradox that the more widely it is recognised that joint information systems are vital to support joint working practices at both micro and macro level, the further such systems seem to be from appearing. This can be partly explained, no doubt, by the clash between the demand for corporate NHS or local authority systems and the need for locally relevant joint systems to support joint working practices across agency boundaries.

Following the NHS and Community Care Act 1990, an apparently comprehensive NHS information strategy was developed. This strategy was widely publicised and covered all aspects of NHS services, yet the only reference to social services or other local authority functions was contained in the specific part of the strategy which focused on "community care". Elsewhere, for example in the sections on hospital systems including discharge there was no mention of the need for dovetailing with social care services, and no suggestion that joint assessment and joint commissioning would need to be supported by the development of joint information systems. Implementing the strategy at local level meant ensuring that information systems in primary care, community and acute services were as far as possible compatible, and had the potential to be interlinked for commissioning and monitoring purposes. The need to integrate systems within the NHS took precedence over the need to integrate systems across care agencies.

Similarly, local authority information systems are likely to be part of a corporate strategy, with mega-deals being struck with hardware companies, for example, and an emphasis on coordinating information across departments rather than with organisations external to the local authority. This drive towards corporate systems is both understandable, and, sadly almost impossible to achieve in practice. This often leaves people in the worst of both worlds, bemoaning the fact that they don't know what is going on within their own organisation, let alone within others.

INFORMATION SYSTEMS AND THEIR POTENTIAL ROLE IN EVALUATING MULTI-AGENCY PROJECTS

In-house systems have in many social services departments been implicitly adapted to take account of care management as it is practised: considerable importance may be attached to recording priority bandings assigned upon referral or allocation, for example. Such measures are introduced for several reasons: to make the best use of limited resources being the most obvious one, but also to make unmanageable caseloads appear more manageable; and to deal with the uncomfortable reality that departments can only meet some of the people's needs some of the time. Considerably less importance may be attached to the *review* aspect of care management, yet without the review process firmly in place, the care management cycle is incomplete. In practice, it seems that most departments are not able to provide enough care managers to ensure that regular review happens at all.

The difficulty occurs when this real life scenario is set against the requirements of data collection for evaluation which seeks to find out whether policy is working in practice. Different reasons for collecting data will inevitably produce different sets of data. In-house information systems are usually geared to monitoring whether statutory duties are being discharged to a high enough standard. Until there is a significant culture shift within the statutory agencies, the criteria for measuring this are likely to continue to be based on professional and managerial judgement rather than on what users and carers want.

It follows from the above that mainstream information systems are of limited value in providing the right sort of data collection systems for evaluating multi-agency projects. Yet the potential of existing systems to meet at least some of the requirements of the evaluation process should be explored as fully as possible, for three main reasons:

1. To see how data from the pilot project can be compared with patterns of service in the mainstream.

2. To inform the further development of in-house information systems to support the development of good practice, and to meet the requirements increasingly being introduced by the expansion of joint working at all levels, from individual assessment to commissioning for populations.

3.   To save valuable staff time, if at all possible, by avoiding duplicating data entry.

Whatever decisions are ultimately taken as to how far existing systems can be used to provide data for evaluation purposes, this may entail a careful balancing act for the evaluation researcher, who needs to get sufficiently involved in the information systems to get optimum data collection without getting <u>too</u> embroiled in either IT systems or the manual data collection systems that feed them. Getting too involved can sidetrack the evaluation researcher from his or her main purpose, which is to get data for the evaluation. Nonetheless, the opportunity is there to bring the fresh perspective of joint agency working onto the development agenda for in-house systems, thereby ensuring more comprehensive and better quality data for the ongoing monitoring of community care in the future.

ADDITIONAL OR ALTERNATIVE FORMS OF DATA COLLECTION FOR EVALUATION

Having decided how far existing information systems can fit the bill, what alternatives are available?   The projects facilitated by SEIPH have all entailed introducing some additional systems to collect the relevant data required to demonstrate key improvements brought about by new ways of working. Whatever data collection system is designed, there are three golden rules:

1. For every item of data, ask, "Why do we want to know this?"
Asking how the data will be used, how the findings might sound, and whether this is truly relevant to the overall aim of project development through ongoing evaluation, will help shape a finite list of items that is manageable and useful, not simply "interesting". Focussing on the overall aim of the research will help to channel resources towards maximum data quality rather than quantity. Even with a clear focus, it will often take a seemingly vast amount of data to demonstrate a key change that can be summed up in a single figure: eg "referrals are dealt with 67% faster using this model as against that model."

2. Consider using manual (paper) systems as well as computers
It is often best to start with a paper system such as a card index to track referrals, then develop a computer system. Starting this way provides a good opportunity for frontline staff to be involved in the design of data collection systems, which can be modified after initial trials. This will give better systems which have benefitted from experienced professional input as well as research skills. Furthermore this will enhance a sense of ownership, leading to better data input.

3. If relying on others to collect and/or input data, keep in close contact
Front line staff are usually very willing in the early stages of a project to take an active part in data collection, but understandably they need support and encouragement as well as occasional trouble-shooting to maintain their initial enthusiasm and level of engagement. They also need very clear guidelines; these should be written down to avoid confusion.

THE PURPOSE OF DATA COLLECTION FOR EVALUATION

All of the data collection systems set up as part of an evaluation will have one common purpose: to demonstrate the benefits and drawbacks of the new arrangements introduced through a multi-agency project. People will usually want to know how well the new arrangements work compared with existing practice, or compared with other similar models of joint working, and so on. Three kinds of comparison are commonly sought.

* comparing performance of care management services before and after attachment to primary care practice(s);

* comparing project performance with mainstream or standard working arrangements;

* comparing different models in different project sites.

All three comparisons pose real difficulties for data collection, although it is probably true to say that the first is the least and the third is the most demanding. In order to manage the complexities of the data collection task, it helps to break it down into component parts of the evaluation. The task of designing the evaluation includes identifying the central *research question*, which underpins the whole evaluation programme; breaking this down into its component parts bearing in mind the need to take all the *stakeholders'* perspectives into account; and choosing the best *research methods* to answer the questions posed for each component. (This is described in the accompanying paper **EVALUATION DESIGN AND ACTION RESEARCH**.) Most of the methods chosen will almost certainly be *qualitative* methods such as interviews, focus groups and document analysis. Two of these methods, and the data collection processes involved, are included at the end of this paper as examples. However, a *quantitative* approach is a principal component in tracking referrals over a period to monitor process and outcomes and make comparisons over time or between models.

DESIGNING MONITORING SYSTEMS TO TRACK REFERRALS

Monitoring for evaluation is similar to ongoing monitoring, and ideally the former will develop into the latter, albeit in a simplified form. Whether you are using a manual system such as a card index, or a computer, the principles of tracking referrals systematically on a case by case basis are the same. For each new referral to the care manager, a new record is created on an index card or in a computer database designed for the purpose. Data collected for each case will need to include, firstly, certain items of basic identifying data (for example name, address, name of GP) which will enable the case to be tracked over time; secondly, items of data which can be analysed and aggregated to give a picture of how well the project is performing. This second group of data items will include, typically, the date of referral, the source of referral, the reason for referral, and details of subsequent action such as date of first contact, date of assessment, outcome of assessment, and date of services being put in place.

Box:5.1   Monitoring data: tracking referrals through the project

1. Length of time elapsed between referral and first visit to get service agreed

2. Number of follow-up calls/ letters required to ensure referral is dealt with

3. Number of people who do not receive services, and reasons

5. Number of first level assessments made from GP practices compared to other sources

6. Quality of first level assessments passed to social services care manager (completeness, appropriateness)

7. Interviews with patients being assessed (plus follow-up after six months)

8. Comparison of costs for care manager outposted to primary care practice, compared with cost of being based in social services local office; accommodation costs, service costs, supervision costs etc., taking into account number of referrals, and any savings.

9. Practice-based care managers' budgets: patterns and trends

10. Routine data collection from social services local offices for comparison: number of first level assessments; by whom; how long between referral and first visit/service implemented.

MANUAL OR COMPUTER DATABASE?

The advantages of a manual card index system are that it is cheap, easy to use, and immediately tangible to everyone using it. The main disadvantage is that whilst individual records may be easy to maintain, the task of analysing the data to calculate time lags and response times, for example, is much more complex involving numerous individual calculations and therefore the time involved in producing an aggregate picture can be prohibitive. The principal advantage of using a computer system is that the task of analysing data, both to complete individual records and to build up a composite picture, is wonderfully simple: provided the database has been designed for the purpose, just a few key presses or mouse clicks will convert dates on each record to a profile of response times over the last six months, for example. The main disadvantages of using computers are that, unless they are already *in situ* within the project office, they are expensive, and staff may require more training and support to use them, or may even be reluctant to use them at all, especially if they are already required to load a similar (but different!) data set into an in-house system.

A third option, which may be a useful "middle way" depending on the balance of resources for the data collection process, is to combine manual and computer systems, with data being entered onto index cards by staff in the project and then regularly copied across by a researcher into the research team's computer for analysis. This involves duplication of data entry, first written, then keyed in but it may be a good compromise if project staff or their managers are unwilling to be involved in two sets of computer input, or where computers are not directly accessible to project staff. An advantage of this option is that by duplicating data entry, there is a good opportunity for the researcher involved to check for continuity and consistency in a thorough but unobtrusive way.

CODED OR UNCODED DATA?

Coding limits the number of possible answers and therefore makes for easier and quicker aggregation of data. However, unless there is a very full understanding of the possible range of answers before the start of data collection, coding can limit the data unnecessarily. As a simple example, the source of referral may be easy to code; the range is defined: eg self, carer, social services office, GP, community nurse (district nurse, health visitor, CPN), practice nurse, other (specify).

FREQUENCY AND COVERAGE

Whilst it might be possible to track every single referral in a project situation, the chances of being able to introduce separate monitoring systems to do this in the mainstream situation (ie to compare results with standard working practice) are low. The options for dealing with this, in order to gather comparative data from mainstream services, include; tracking all referrals over a shorter time interval; routinely tracking a sample of referrals, say a 10% sample; or tracking all referrals but selecting one local office only. It is not ideal to mix data collection intervals, but in practice this may be the most workable solution.

For example, in the project described in the next box, we were able to loosely compare the data collected by routine monitoring over a year within the project sites with just one month's data from the district office. This limited the validity of the findings, but in the absence of a viable alternative it was the best option.

The key is to be open about the fact that the data has been collected in this way, and to acknowledge the limitations of any comparisons made. In the example cited, the improvement in response times in the project as compared with standard practice was as much as tenfold: even allowing for the district office month not being typical in some way, it could safely be concluded that the project was successful in this respect! An enhancement would have been to repeat the one month data collection in the district office at the end of the data collection year, depending on the willingness of district based staff to do this.

SAMPLING AND SELECTION

Whilst you may be in a position to collect basic monitoring data on everyone who is referred throughout the duration of the project, it is unlikely that you will be able to achieve universal coverage for the comparative part of the exercise, ie the referrals that are dealt with via traditional working arrangements through the social services district office. So deciding on a sampling strategy is important. Decisions on sampling and selection may also be needed for other parts of the evaluation research. For example, depending on the size of the project and the scale of evaluation resources, it may be decided to interview a selected group of staff from each discipline at regular intervals, or at the beginning and end of the project, rather than trying to cover the whole staff.

There are several approaches to sampling, which fall into two broad categories; *probability* and *non-probability sampling. Probability sampling,* provided your sample size is appropriate, will enable you to generalise from results gained within the sample to the likely span of results for the whole population. The best known technique in this category is random sampling, but there are other methods, such as cluster sampling, stratified sampling and systematic sampling. All of these methods depend on having a sampling frame, ie a list of all the possible cases to be included. For example, the patient list held by a GP practice is a sampling frame for the patient population. If, however, you do not have a sampling frame to use, or if you do not consider it necessary or relevant to select a sample that is representative of the whole population, then there are other sampling techniques such as quota sampling, snowballing, or convenience sampling. What is important is to know why you have adopted a particular approach to sampling, and what limitations your approach may place on the validity of the results.

Box : 5.2   Samples and responses: an example
(NB This example has been slightly modified for illustrative purposes)

Prior to setting up pilot projects to test different models of joint working, a London health authority commissioned a baseline survey to find out how well community care arrangements were working from the perspective of professionals in the primary health care team. A 50% sample was taken, using the list of practices supplied by the health authority as the sampling frame. The list was divided into locality groups, and every other primary care practice on the list was sent a postal questionnaire. The initial overall response rate was just over 28% of the sample, which was poor but not unexpected from a postal survey to this particular target group. GPs are a heavily researched group, prone to survey overkill! However, when the response rate was analysed by locality, there was a wide variation, from under 20% in one locality to over 40% in another. To boost the response and widen the spread, a second (repeat) questionnaire was sent to all who had not replied, with a covering letter explaining how important it was to get the views of primary care teams in all localities. By good fortune, the final response rate was fairly well balanced at around 35% across all four localities: still low, but at least giving a more representative spread.

Terminology:
In this example, the *population of interest* was all the primary care practices in the borough (NB: the health authority covered more than one borough, but there was some coterminosity between the primary care localities and the local authority borough boundaries). The *sampling frame* was the list of practices kept by the health authority. The *sample size* was 45 (ie 50% of the total number of practices), to ensure an adequate response rate without overstretching the time available for analysis. The sample was *stratified* according to locality, to ensure that 50% of practices in each locality were included in the sample. This was considered necessary because the localities varied considerably, from inner city localities to leafy suburbs). Alternative sampling strategies could have considered stratifying according to post-code district, or - taking a different dimension - according to the number of GPs in the practice (ie to ensure representative coverage of single-handed and group practices, for example).

TRACKING REFERRALS: AN EXAMPLE

In a three year project which set out to test two different models for integrating care management within primary care teams, a part time researcher was appointed to collect and analyse data from about twenty primary care practices. Some practices had a named care manager linked to the practice but still based in a social services local office; referrals were dealt with in the traditional way, via the local office allocation process, and the care manager's role in relation to the primary health care team was primarily a liaison role. Other practices or clusters of smaller practices had a care manager based in the practice (or based in a central practice in the case of clusters); all referrals relating to patients of the practice(s) were dealt with by the care manager, who had a support worker also based in the practice to deal with administration and to liaise with social services administrative systems as necessary.

The evaluation of these two models included a tracking exercise, with the aim of demonstrating over a full year (the second year of the project) the pattern of response times following referral in the different practices and with different working arrangements. It transpired early on that the in-house system was not able to provide the level of information which would enable us to track referrals via the local social services office (ie for the practice-linked care management model), so this part of the exercise was abandoned; owing to time constraints, a one month "snapshot" set of data was collected from a local office as a proxy measure for comparison instead. The full tracking exercise was carried out by the three practice-based care managers, who covered a total of ten practices.

Monitoring started in the developmental year, with a manual database system simply recording the user's name, address, date of birth and date of referral onto a card index. Later, in preparation for the full twelve months of data collection during the second year of the project, a computer database was designed by the researcher. The content was similar to that of the index cards, with the addition of a few additional fields, such as the source of referral, the priority assigned on referral (according to social services standard procedures in the borough) and the priority assigned on assessment. Within a short time, the database was already in need of modification, because the monitoring of priority changes between referral and assessment proved unmanageable and largely irrelevant, since the practice-based care manager was able to turn cases around so fast that the assignment of priorities was a purely paper exercise: all cases were being dealt with within a number of days.

Further modifications were introduced, to include a monthly print out of cases which were due for review, and to allow for the "date of first contact" to be recorded: this is the date when the care manager telephones the client (or visits, in cases which are known to be urgent) to make an appointment for the assessment visit. This initial contact already seemed to be an important aspect of the practice-based care managers' new way of working: in the district office, the time lag between referral and allocation meant that all non-urgent cases would wait at least some days for confirmation that the referral had been received, whereas in the project, every client was being contacted within a couple of days at most.

Despite initial and some ongoing concern about the amount of time taken to track referrals in this way, care managers and their seniors soon saw the advantages of being able to analyse their own data, and began to ask for new fields to be added and new reports to be constructed. This interactive approach to designing computer systems to monitor activity was experienced very positively by those involved. Once professionals had gained confidence in the competence of the project team in collecting data for the evaluation in a way which also gave them useful insight into their own working practices, the task of the evaluation researcher was then to ensure that these two aspects were in balance, and that the system was still collecting all the data needed for the evaluation as well as producing data for the professionals involved to use for their own operational purposes.

COMPARING NEW WORKING ARRANGEMENTS WITH STANDARD PRACTICE: AN EXAMPLE

An evaluation of new models of service delivery or new working arrangements for example in multi-disciplinary teams will usually seek to compare the performance of the new system with the standard arrangements operating in mainstream services. The difficulties of getting good comparative data should not be underestimated, however. One of the main difficulties encountered is that standard information systems are not normally able to generate data to compare with the data being collected specifically for the project. One reason for this is that different working arrangements lend themselves to recording different items.

For example, in the projects facilitated by SEIPH, a key factor for success in attaching care management to primary care practices has been the capacity for the care manager to respond quickly in making a first contact with the client following referral. This first contact may be a phone call or, in potentially urgent cases, a visit. It appears that this swift personal response from professional to client is of some discrete benefit in itself, both to the client and to health care professionals, whose confidence in the care management process is enhanced. This hypothesis has not yet been tested as such in our projects, and to do so would be difficult owing to the different monitoring systems in place. In mainstream working arrangements ie where all referrals are dealt with at the local social services office via a system of duty and allocation the date of first contact is neither noted nor recorded. What is more likely to be recorded is the date of allocation. The time lapse from referral to allocation may not only be a useful measure of performance within the organisation, but is also of direct consequence to the client's well-being. This also highlights the fact that projects exploring the merits of joint working models are not simply testing different working arrangements, they are studying the impact of a different ethos.

Where you are able to gather comparative data, useful indicators for comparison with standard working arrangements are caseload and response times, so that findings can be summarised in tabular form:

COMPARING CASELOAD INFORMATION

Indicator	Standard working arrangements (eg all referrals dealt with at district office)	Multi-agency project (eg care manager based in primary care practice)
No. of staff per 10,000 pop.		
Caseload per 10,000 pop.		
No. of highest priority cases per 10,000 pop.		

Each of these apparently straightforward indicators requires careful consideration, however. Definitions of what constitutes a case may need to be clarified: for example, this is often defined in Social Service Departments as having been officially opened by being recorded on "the system". In traditional practice, this usually excludes any potential cases which are dealt with at the duty officer stage as well as potential cases dealt with prior to this, at telephone or reception stage. By contrast, a care manager attached to a practice may be liable to take all incoming calls (particularly in the early stages) and may legitimately count them as cases. For consistency of comparison, it will be best to discount these additional "not-quite-cases", but it is also important to recognise that in these circumstances, what is being compared is caseload, not workload. Caseload can only be used as a proxy measure of workload where the same style of practice is being observed. A care manager based in a primary care practice is likely to operate in a different way, dealing with more referrals directly as they come in, and therefore turning over more cases before they are even recorded on the social services standard information system. Furthermore, a care manager in a health centre may offer one-off information and advice sessions, which are unlikely to be recorded on the system. All this needs to be included in the data collection design, both for evaluation and ongoing monitoring purposes.

COMPARING RESPONSE TIMES

Indicator	Standard working arrangements (eg all referrals dealt with at District Office)	Multi-agency Project (eg Care Manager based in primary care practice)
Average no. of days from referral to first contact		
Average no. of days from first contact to assessment		
Average no. of days from assessment to service delivery		
Average no. of days in total from referral to service delivery		

COMPARING "BEFORE AND AFTER" NEW WORKING PRACTICES: AN EXAMPLE

This example illustrates how qualitative and quantitative data collection methods can be interwoven in an evaluation. The list in box 5.3 comprises the set of data items collected as part of a baseline profile exercise carried out in each primary care practice to be included in a three year project covering practice-based care management for older people and disabled adults.

Items 1-3 describe the basic demographic and epidemiological breakdown of the practice's patient population. These are straightforward quantitative data, gathered as far as possible from practice profiles and analysis of practice-held records; practices vary as to the accuracy of recording the disability status of their patients, however.

Items 4-7 describe the pre-project pattern of referral and response in relation to social services. They are also quantitative data, which may need to be collected from a selected sample of patient notes (ie a random sample of notes for older patients and patients with disabilities, if these are the groups to be covered by the project) .

Item 8 the number of follow-up contacts to chase referral through, may not be routinely recorded, so some estimate may be gathered from staff, or a simple manual recording system could be set up in the month prior to project start-up.

Item 9 contains a quantitative element ("number of people who do not receive services...") and a qualitative element ("... and reasons"). It is unlikely that both will be routinely recorded in patients' notes, so these may need to be gathered by the same manual recording system as item 8.

Items 10 and 11 rely on qualitative data which need to be collected by methods such as in-

---

Box: 5.3   **"Before and after" comparison**
Baseline information for evaluating multi-agency projects

1. Age & gender profile of patients 18+

2. Age & gender profile of patients aged 65+ and 75+

3. Age & gender profile of patients aged 18+ with physical disabilities

4. Number of referrals made by the practice team to social services in respect of older people aged 65+ and 75+, and disabled adults

5. Number of days from referral to first contact

6. Number of days from first contact to assessment

7. Number of days from assessment to service delivery

8. Number of follow-up calls or letters required to ensure referral is dealt with

9. Number of people who do not receive services, and reasons

10. Views of care managers and primary health care team regarding perceived roles and responsibilities, and expectations of the project (anticipated benefits and problems)

11. Views of service users and carers regarding past and current experience of social services; care management; and primary health care.

USING INTERVIEWS FOR EVALUATION FROM THE PERSPECTIVE OF STAFF: AN EXAMPLE

This example illustrates how overlapping exercises in comparison can be useful, so long as they are handled carefully. It also highlights how data collection needs to be flexible in response to changing circumstances, whilst maintaining some fixed elements to ensure that valid comparisons can still be made.

The evaluation related to a two stage locality based project. The data collection method was a telephone interview, using a semi-structured interview schedule. At the beginning of the first stage of the project, a broadly representative sample of primary care staff from all the practices involved and social services staff from the district office relating to that locality, were interviewed individually, using the schedule summarised in box 5.4. The data from this set of interviews were analysed, and the researcher produced a detailed descriptive (and anonymised) record of staff feedback, this gave the project manager a full picture of their collective views, broken down by different professional groups, in order for her to take the appropriate action to develop the project. At the end of the first stage of the project, a second set of interviews was carried out with the same sample of staff. This time a much simpler and shorter interview schedule was used, with the focus on three key items identified by staff in the first round as in need of attention if the project was to succeed. The reason for using a shorter schedule summarised in box 5.5 was to reduce the demand on staff time, to thereby maintain a good response rate, and to simplify the process of analysis.

The second stage of the project involved the same primary care practices, but by this time specific care managers were identified with particular practices in a liaison capacity, while still being based in the local social services office. Meanwhile, other models of linking care management to primary care were being explored in other parts of the borough, and the multi-agency steering group was interested in comparing the different models if possible. With this in mind, the third set of interviews summarised in box 5.6 was carried out at the end of the second stage. This allowed us to compare across two dimensions: firstly across time, by interviewing the original set of staff and managers for a third time; and secondly across different models, by including a new sample of staff and managers from outside the project who were involved in alternative joint working models elsewhere in the borough.

Box:5.4   **First interview schedule (staff and managers)**

This schedule was drawn up for use in telephone interviews carried out at the beginning of stage I of the project.

Name: Date: Length of interview: .... minutes

1.   Which agency employs you?
2.   How long have you been with this agency?
3.   What is your job title?
4.   How long have you been in this post?
5.   To whom are you immediately accountable?
6.   Which team (or teams) do you belong to?
7.   What geographical catchment area does your work cover?
8.   How would you describe your role
     a) in general?
     b) in relation to community care assessments and care planning?
9.   What is your understanding of the project?
10. Do you know who else is involved in the project?
11. How would you describe how care management (or joint assessment) work? eg. Whose needs might be assessed? By whom? What is included? Who else is involved? How is the information recorded? What happens next?

12. What are the main features that make the new way of working (in the project) different from standard working arrangements for people who might need community care services?

13. How do you think these new ways of working will affect:

     a) people who need services, and carers?

     b) you in your work?

     c) colleagues in your organisation?

     d) colleagues in other organisations directly involved in the project?

     e) other organisations not directly involved in the project?

14. What do you see as the main benefits of the new arrangements introduced by the project?

15. Are there any disadvantages?

16. What do you see as the main difficulties to be sorted out in the near future?

17. Can you tell me about any training you have received in relation to the new arrangements?

18. Do you have any other comments?

Box:5.5   **Second interview schedule (staff and managers)**

This short interview schedule was designed for use at the end of Stage I of the project. It addressed the key issues identified in the first round, and was effectively an interim step in the "before" and "after" comparison which was central to the evaluation.

Name:
Post:
Employing organisation:

Date...............................   Length of interview................................minutes

Q1.   COMMUNICATION

Communication (about referrals, assessments and structural changes in organisations and teams) was identified as a key area for improvement according to the interviews held at the start of the project. Have there been any changes since then, do you think:

a) in your own organisation?

b) in other organisations?

Q2   TRAINING

Training about the new arrangements for assessment was another area highlighted in earlier interviews as in need of further action. How has the situation changed since then?

a) Have you been offered any training?

b) Have you received any training?

c) If so, was it useful?

Q3   ASSESSMENT

a) What is your role in obtaining health or social care services for patients/service users?

b) How has this changed since you were last interviewed (six months ago)?

c) What further improvements are needed, and how can these be carried out?

Box: 5.6   **Third interview schedule (staff and managers)**

This schedule was drawn up for use in telephone interviews carried out at the end of stage 2 of the project. The purpose of this third set of interviews was to follow on from the "before and after" interviews carried out at the beginning and end of Stage 1 and also to compare feedback from project staff and managers with feedback from staff and managers involved with alternative models outside the project.

Name: Date: Length of interview: .... minutes

1.   Which organisation employs you?
2.   How long have you been with this agency?
3.   What is your job title?
4.   How long have you been in this post?
5.   To whom are you immediately accountable?
6.   Which team (or teams) do you belong to?
7.   What geographical catchment area does your work cover?
8.   What is your role in relation to community care assessments and care planning?
9.   Which joint working arrangements/projects/models are you familiar with in the borough?

10.   I would like to ask you some questions about the joint working project or model you are most familiar with. (Imagine you are describing the project to a colleague who is familiar with community care but not directly involved in the project/model).

   a)   How does the project/model work?
   b)   How does it differ from working arrangements elsewhere?
   c)   How well do you think it works for service users and carers?
   d)   What about its specific impact on particular groups?
             Elderly people; elderly people with mental health problems, including dementia; people with physical disabilities; people with mental illness; people with learning disabilities; people with HIV/AIDS; children with special needs
   e)   How are patterns of referrals, assessments and services monitored at present?
   f)   How do you think the project impacts on staff and managers?
   g)   Can you add any specific comments relating to:
             training; supervision and support; cover for absence through holidays and sickness; communication issues; line management and accountability; information sharing; links with other agencies; accessing budgets; overall coordination?
   h)   Do you think the project/model would be worth transferring to other areas?
   i)   What changes in the project/model would help it run more effectively?

TRAINING REQUIREMENTS AND RECOGNITION AT THE CROSSROADS OF HEALTH AND SOCIAL CARE

INTRODUCTION

This paper reflects on SEIPH's experience in the development of work-based multi-disciplinary training programmes for qualified and unqualified staff working together for the first time. Most of the joint working focussed on the first stages of information gathering associated with the identification of individual needs during the community care assessment process. Initially, the training addressed the overall objectives of the joint assessment and care management pilots which were being developed as lead initiatives. As the joint working developed, issues would be raised which formed the content of later training.

The multi-disciplinary developments shared several characteristics:

- primary health and social care professionals were brought into formal collaboration;

- professionals were required to develop better understandings of each other's work;

- information systems were developed which reflected the closer working relationships of the professionals involved;

- every pilot was part of a larger project managed by an independent consultant who was responsible to a multi-agency steering group with senior representatives from participating or interested agencies.

Each initiative was designed to be flexible and responsive to local circumstances. For the most part, they involved social services care managers for older people establishing formal relationships within primary health care providers, mainly GP practice teams. The pilots were characterised by one of three relationships of this type, where care managers were either:

linked to GP practices, but based in social services local offices;
regular meetings with GPs and practice staff enabled multi-disciplinary discussion to information share; discuss individual care; arrange joint assessments where appropriate; encourage reduction of inappropriate referrals.
OR

<u>aligned</u> with GP practices, but based in social services local offices;
care management caseload consisting of patients from the GP practice, irrespective of point of referral (practice or social services office); care manager provides social care "surgeries" for clients

OR

<u>attached</u> to the GP practice by being based in the practice as a member of the primary care team, though remaining employed by social services

The pilots did not remain static. What began as experiments in linked working relationships often moved quite quickly to aligned or attached arrangements as participants began to experience the benefits of joint working. Pilots beginning later in the programme were taken forward by participants who opted to bypass the linked phase completely, so that immediate engagement with the aligned or attached model became possible.

PROJECT OBJECTIVES

The overall aim of the project was to maintain or improve the health and social functioning of the service user, by the provision of coordinated and efficient health and social care. This was to be achieved by:

- developing positive and informed relationships amongst professionals;

- designing and implementing common procedures across agency boundaries;

- reducing duplication of activity and inappropriate referrals;

- integrating social care capability into primary health care teams;

- providing opportunities for service users and carers to be more fully involved in the planning of their services;

- evaluating the effectiveness of the new models of joint working.

These became the objectives of the project pilots and the basis on which the training was designed, facilitated and later modified.

TRAINING OBJECTIVES

The training objectives closely mirrored the derived objectives of the project pilots. All training was designed to develop clear understandings of the project aim and objectives across agency boundaries. To some extent, early training involved developing a common language. Identical terms carried differing meanings between agencies, and it was essential that variations in meaning were exposed and not allowed to obscure the objectives.

There were ten overall objectives of the training:

1.   to promote better understanding of the differing professional skills and roles within the pilot teams;
2.   to identify similar organisational processes which could be exploited by the pilot teams;
3.   to identify dissimilar organisational processes which required management or alteration;
4.   to become familiar with differing policy objectives as they impacted on the work of the pilots;
5.   to clarify the legal foundations of the project pilots;
6.   to identify obstacles likely to frustrate joint working;
7.   to identify good practice which would promote joint working;
8.   to identify good communication processes and/or suggest improvements;
9.   to provide initial information regarding the design of the project evaluation and identify data sources essential to the evaluation process;
10.   to consult with participating professionals about the development of a joint human resources development strategy.

The competencies every participant would develop at the end of the initial training series included:

•   a full understanding of the implications of the NHS & Community Care Act 1990 for the work of the pilot teams;

•   an appreciation of the skills and experience of the different professionals;

•   a developed perspective of the importance of working as a team in the provision of community based health and social care;

•   the development of useful relationships which promote effective communication and assist problem-solving in community care settings.

The training provided was in every case multi-disciplinary, and in most cases provided for the teams which would be working together. The training was PGEA approved for six hours of each day's training, making it an attractive option for busy GPs. Training the teams individually proved to be the most effective model for meeting the training objectives. Every training session concluded with the development of an action plan to take forward issues raised during the training session.

CONTENT OF THE TRAINING

The content of the training developed as the project pilots progressed. As participants began to understand the implications of joint working for their practice, new issues arose which required investigation and discussion. Subsequent training was specifically designed to address issues which arose within individual pilots as well as across all the pilots.

Initial training

This took place immediately before or just after the pilot teams were formed. It would typically be a single day session with a follow up day within three to four weeks. After introductions, the typical content would include:

- the project pilot's aims and objectives;

- the relationship of the pilots to the NHS & Community Care Act 1990;

- "What people do all day!" an exercise that both tests participant's knowledge of each other's professional roles and clarifies those roles;

- models of multi-disciplinary assessment of need;

- the description of skills required for joint assessment and joint working;

- the initial identification of skills available within the pilot team;

- thinking through how essential skills not available within the team (if any) could be developed or accessed;

- the initial development of common values within the project team.

The initial training focused on developing explicit shared understandings of the project's purpose and of the basic functions to be undertaken by the pilots. Strong emphasis was placed on the development of common values, as professionals and people generally are more motivated by their values than anything else. Values were defined as statements of good practice which serve the achievement of the project purpose.

Subsequent training

Formal training was provided to each of the pilots at four to six month intervals throughout the pilots. Again, each was designed to explore issues and resolve problems which arose during the pilot process. Typical of the issues examined were:

- empowerment of staff and service users;

- service user and carer participation in planning and monitoring services;

- new models of team learning and information sharing;

- new models of joint assessment;

- the advocacy role of the professional;

- workload management techniques;

- equal opportunity issues;

- identifying and recording unmet needs;

- techniques for problem identification and management;

- measuring effectiveness of services.

Most of the problems which arose concerned communication systems and procedural issues. There were problems with:

- maintaining communication with linked care managers (few problems occurred with aligned or attached care managers);

- duplication of information on multiple forms, which served the same function but for different agencies;

- communication within agencies about the activity and effects of the pilots;

- communication across agencies to senior levels about the value of the pilots;

- job description revision and update;

- data collection problems relating to information required for the evaluation.

All subsequent training was limited to half-day sessions, with many events involving GPs. They were designed to be practical and, again, concluded with an action planning discussion.

Final training

Final training addressed the transition from pilot project to mainstream services. The evaluation was by this time providing powerful information about both the effectiveness of the projects and the efficiency of joint working, and agencies were thinking in terms of establishing linked or aligned care managers within primary health care teams throughout the borough. The pilot sites would then develop programmes to "roll out" their new and now tested joint working processes to other localities.

Final training was designed to briefly review the progress of the pilots and identify action plans for the subsequent roll-out. The issues typically considered during final training included:

- identification of the achievements of the pilots;

- review of problems which arose during the pilots:
  - their causes
  - their effects
  - how they were resolved
  - why they might be persisting

- the acknowledgement of lessons learned during the pilot;

- developing strategies for rolling out joint assessment and joint working throughout the borough.

EFFECT OF THE TRAINING

The three stages of training were designed to meet the initial and emerging needs of the pilots. During these stages, issues were identified and examined and problems resolved by negotiation within or across the pilot groups. The training was designed to support the experience of joint assessment and joint working, and it was this experience which proved more positive than had been expected. Primary health care teams evolved into "primary care teams" which fully incorporated social care professionals as team members. The sense of boundary or demarcation between agencies diminished in importance within the pilot teams, while remaining problematical in localities not served by the pilots.

The relevance of the training itself was confirmed by the overall success of the pilots. Participants felt the training regarding theoretical and practical matters had been well focused and relatively unobtrusive in their already busy lives. The pilot teams readily participated is setting the agendas for subsequent and final training events, and were enthusiastic in their discussion of project-wide issues as well as those directly relating to their own pilot. The training provided forums for these busy and enthusiastic people to think through the implications of their experience for themselves as professionals and for the future of joint service provision. Subsequent and final training events were characterised by observation of and reflection about the experience of multi-disciplinary team working, so that it became difficult (and probably unproductive) to identify whether it was the experience or the training that was effective; it was both together.

Two significant unintended issues arose from this model of reflective training. Whilst one related to the longer term objectives of multi-disciplinary services and the other to the needs of individual practitioners, both were characterised by a looking forward. These issues were:

> the development of a vision of future service provision;

> the development of specialised and recognised training programmes for practitioners working in multi-disciplinary settings.

These issues are taken up in the next two sections.

DEVELOPING A VISION OF FUTURE SERVICE PROVISION

The need for a "corporate" vision

Logically, activity should follow intention. This was not the case with the project pilots. The agencies, though negotiating and compromising in the establishment of the pilots, had limited enthusiasm for and therefore narrow experience of collaborative working. Their differing processes and objectives as well as distinct planning timescales provided a barrier that proved difficult to overcome, because it also afforded comfort and an (illusory) sense of stability. Only after the experience and training of the pilots could the benefits be acknowledged as benefits for all the participating agencies. If those common benefits were to be maintained in the future, a new approach to planning must be adopted, which reflected the original intentions behind the community care planning mechanisms already in existence, but which until then had remained peripheral to operational experience.

The project steering group accepted that the development of a common vision for future services had not only become desirable, but essential if the benefits of multi-disciplinary working were to be maintained. Funding for the pilots was to end, and inter-agency agreements were required to ensure resources were available following the pilot period.

Developing the vision

The key agencies represented on the steering group did not represent all the agencies that needed to participate in defining a vision of future services. For this task other groups were to be represented, including:

- local authority housing officers;
- occupational therapists;
- service user groups and service users;
- carers groups.

This extended steering group met under independent facilitation to begin to construct a "vision statement." Looking forward five years, the group established the foundations of a document which would set out an imaginative but realistic insight into the possible quality of life enhancements it wished to provide for service users at that time. The term "vision" seemed rather too messianic for some, who preferred to call the document a "futures statement".

The approach was straight forward. The group met and considered these questions:

- In what directions are the pilots moving?

- What new capabilities has joint working established in the pilots?
      What have been the effects of these capabilities?
      Are the capabilities generalisable to other localities or client groups?

- What should health and social care provision look like:
      in two years?
      in five years?

- What strategy needs to be in place, how do we get there from here?
      What needs to be done?
      Who needs to be influenced?
      Who needs to be involved?

- What are the next steps, action planning

Who needs to do what?
With whom?
By when?

Major themes for the future

Seven themes emerged relating to the characteristics of future services:

Working as a team

Health and social care professionals, including a wide range of specialist service providers, will be engaging with and around the service user as members of the service user's team.

Shared information

Information systems will have been developed which allow service users and professionals to have direct access to all *appropriate* information relating to health and social care needs and service requirements.

An "achievement" culture

A new atmosphere will exist where empowerment and capability development overcome preoccupations with service provision processes.

The shared use of resources

Because shared funding of joint initiatives will be commonplace and internal procedural barriers will be minimised, service users' access to resources will not be restricted by artificial organisational processes.

Single service access points

Services could be requested, reviewed or altered by contacting any one of the participating agencies.

Coordinated planning cycles

All health and social care agencies' planning will be coordinated in three-year planning cycles, with annual reviews and adjustments.

Effective partnerships

Service users and carers will be actively contributing to the strategic evolution of primary and community care as well as active CHCs and independent service providers.

Major changes required to bring the vision to reality

Specific strategies would be required to achieve three major changes if the vision of the future was to become the reality of the future:

Equity of service provision

Service users must be able to benefit from equity of access to services irrespective of where or how they live. Convenient locally accessible and locally grouped facilities for primary and community care assessment and services become a planning priority. Services which are sufficiently flexible to meet individual needs can be provided within eligibility criteria but without discrimination and prejudice on the basis of locality, disability or personal behaviour.

Service user acceptance and use of power

Service users must be well informed about the range of services which relate to their needs, the alternatives to those services and whether they are available locally. Better information raises expectations but also helps expectations remain realistic. Service users and their carers must be encouraged and *expected* to negotiate for choice in the services or treatments of preference, following professional assessment.

Collaboration rather than simply consultation

Service users and their carers must be equipped to act in partnership with professionals to ensure that service emphases are on the development and maintenance of the capabilities which underpin quality of life. Productive partnerships are founded on communication that initiates a sense of working and planning together. Dialogue is not enough. It is joint action which diminishes suspicion and develops trust.

THE DEVELOPMENT OF SPECIALISED AND RECOGNISED TRAINING FOR PRACTITIONERS WORKING IN MULTI-DISCIPLINARY SETTINGS

Working in multi-disciplinary teams is not necessarily difficult, but it is different! Professional training is only beginning to emphasize the multi-disciplinary aspect of community care. Maintaining individual professional perspectives is essential to good team working, as long as single perspectives are not allowed to consistently dominate a team's approach to service provision.

Three ideas emerged as a result of the project pilots and the supporting training:

the production of a joint human resources development (HRD) strategy;

the development of new models of joint assessment and associated training;

the development of joint training national awards for unqualified staff.

A joint HRD strategy

The projects were able to access funding provided by the NHS Training Division and the Local Government Management Board to develop a strategy for implementing a programme of developing skills across the participating agencies. Complementing existing training programmes within each agency, this strategy addressed the implementation of core training and development programmes, providing a foundation for joint assessment and joint working amongst professionals. The purpose of the strategy was to establish the core skills and information bases essential to the development of well informed and motivated teams. The aim was to extend the capability of team members to provide services which their service users would recognise as being "seamless".

The strategy specified that training and development programmes would provide learning experiences for professionals from a range of different disciplines who are working as a team. These experiences were to be work-based and the theoretical underpinnings were to relate to the actual work of the locality. The skills and knowledge bases developed would be appropriate contributions to a personal portfolio leading to NVQ recognition.

The structure of the strategy remained simple. The principles underpinning the joint services also formed the foundation of the strategy. They were that:

1   services are based on individual and personal needs as identified and agreed with the service user;
2   service users will have accurate and full information to help them make choices about their services;
3   all people will have equal access to the services;
4   people will be treated with courtesy, honesty and respect;
5   quality means that how services are provided is as important as the services themselves;

6   each professional assessment of need will be acceptable to all purchasing agencies;

7   service users will be invited to help evaluate the quality of services;

8   services will be sensitive to accommodate the changing needs of service users.

The strategy identified the core skills bases required by staff who will have completed a training and development programme. The training was to be designed in such a way as to enable the participants to demonstrate their abilities to:

- participate in an agreed multi-disciplinary assessment process;

- work as part of a multi-agency team;

- communicate effectively and assertively;

- collect and record assessment and service information effectively, including information on unmet need;

- establish purposeful networks amongst care agencies working in their localities;

- process service requests to the appropriate agencies or teams;

- monitor the progress of care plans and the achievement of targets;

- develop alternatives to address unmet need;

- apply protocols relating to confidentiality to their daily work.

Essential knowledge bases were also identified as required elements of the training and development programmes. Participants would be required to demonstrate a working knowledge of:

- the benefits and problems associated with joint working in their locality;

- the NHS & Community Care Act 1990, with particular reference to the rights of service users;

- relevant policies and procedures of all participating agencies;

- the roles, responsibilities and constraints of each of the major care agencies in their locality;

- criteria of eligibility for services within their locality;

- the differing and complementary skills and expertise of the various professional disciplines with which they are working;

- confidentiality policies and protocols;

- resources available.

The specific range of topics identified in the strategy related to three fundamental concepts. The interweaving of these topics throughout the programme would provide learning opportunities that were relevant to the achievement of the core skills and knowledge bases. Within each topic area would be themes to be examined in relation to the participants' experience.

Competence

    avoiding duplication
    negotiation
    problem analysis and problem solving
    support for service users facing difficult treatments or life changing decisions
    support for carers
    working as a team "around" the service user
    evaluating the effectiveness of services with the service user
    helping others manage change

Confidence

    identification of areas of potential conflict
    conflict management
    managing resistance
    equal opportunities policies and issues
    best employment practices
    improving job satisfaction amongst practitioners
    managing change

Communication

    clarifying and simplifying access to services
    streamlining communication amongst agencies
    effective interviewing techniques

sharing confidential information

Developing the joint HRD strategy built on the experience in the pilots, where philosophical or procedural differences amongst agencies had already been identified and managed. It was essential that the development of the strategy did not impact already heavy workloads, so discussions were facilitated independently and took place within the cycle of pre-arranged meetings.

Joint assessment training

The need for joint assessment training became clear at the time of the initial training. To respond to this need, as well as anticipating the requirement for such training in the near future, SEIPH in collaboration with Positive Publications, Brighton produced ASSESSMENT: WORKING AS A TEAM, a video assisted training pack for multi-disciplinary assessment of need within four major client groups:

> older people;
> people with physical disabilities;
> people with mental health problems;
> people with learning disabilities.

The pack, including overhead displays, training notes and practitioners' guide (which could be purchased separately) was designed as a five day programme to be provided over a three to five week period. Each day addressed a particular theme and built a foundation for the following days.

Day 1 Teamwork

Teamwork is based on the convergence of the skills, intentions and expectations of team members. To achieve the necessary "common language" and shared understandings necessary for effective team work, the focus of day 1 was on the negotiation of statements regarding the team's purpose, values and major functions.

Day 2 Assessment: professional roles

Effective joint assessments require coordinated participation of a range of health and social care professionals. Every participant must fully understand the other's professional roles, and how differing agency requirements impact on professional activities and responsibilities.

Day 3 Assessment: Core Skills

This addresses the component parts of assessment in detail, in terms both of the factors to be considered during the assessment process and the skills required. Personal action plans are developed for each team member, identifying skills to be acquired or developed, how that could be done, and the date by which that development will be completed.

Day 4 Organizing the team's skills

This builds directly on the foundation of the previous days by identifying who in the team has the skills required for joint assessment. No one person is likely to have all the skills needed, and many team members will wish to develop new skills. This may require team working practices to be modified to ensure that allocation of assessment tasks is based on the skills available rather than job description or seniority.

Day 5 Evaluation

Moving forward as a team should mean that the team is able to incorporate the ability to monitor its own effectiveness. Simple self-evaluation methods based on action research models help team members monitor performance against the agreed purpose and values of the team.

The development of joint training national awards in care for unqualified staff

Many of the participating staff had no professional social or health care qualification. It became clear during subsequent training in the pilot teams that a strategy for the development of unqualified staff was required, and that training provided could be within the National Vocational Qualification framework. This was also in line with the joint HRD strategy recently developed. It became a primary objective to establish a secondary pilot for this training in which the required core and endorsement units could be assembled or designed which could enable unqualified participants to demonstrate the competences required to achieve NVQ Level 3 "Promoting Independence". Provided through a "distance learning" model, the training would be managed by an agency with appropriate experience and expertise in such models. In this case, this was the Joint Initiative for Community Care Ltd.

Central to the training content was a module developed specifically addressing the issues of multi-disciplinary working. It was designed to enable participants to demonstrate abilities to:

- work as part of a multi-agency team;

- collect and record basic information using locally agreed formats and procedures;

- pass service requests to the correct agencies or disciplines;

- establish purposeful relationships with agencies in the locality.

Participants were also required to demonstrate knowledge and understanding of:

- the value and benefits of joint working;

- joint working as applied specifically to their own pilot locality;

- the NHS & Community Care Act 1990 as it applies to the rights of the patient;

- the roles, responsibilities, constraints and service criteria of relevant local agencies;

- similarities, differences and demarcations amongst agencies;

- the differing and complementary skills and expertise of the various professional disciplines.

This was a major development which required related but independent project management. Suitable training materials were produced in partnership with the National Extension College and application for recognition as an assessment centre was made to and accepted by City and Guilds. The aims of the NVQ training were completely consistent with all National Council for Vocational Qualifications (NCVQ) requirements in that its intention is to:

- improve the value of qualifications to employers and participants;

- encourage participants to develop competence by improving access to qualifications through training;

- encourage provision of effective education by providing for the "real world" needs of both participants and employers.

The participants' progress accelerated as they became more familiar with the NVQ processes. The assessors who continued throughout the project achieved NVQ awards themselves as recognized competent assessors.

CONCLUSION

Whether it is the training that strengthens joint working, or joint working that enhances the training, both will benefit. Those working on pilot projects themselves proved to be effective participants in the training design team, as well as testers and beneficiaries of the training programmes. The development of the whole approach to training became interactive, reflecting the working of the teams. They contributed to the design of their own training, where the emphasis was to be on management, not measurement; where the concern was the control of the work, not the worker; and where opportunities to empower were valued above those that offered only containment.

INDEX

This is not an exhaustive index. It is intended to help locate key topics and points of interest in the text. It does not include terms occurring very frequently throughout the text, such as 'information' or 'project'. Main subject headings can be found by consulting the contents page.